PRAISE FOR ALICE MCCALL'S *'Wellness Wisdom'* APPROACH

"Alice's healing approach works. I suffered with IBS, Irritable Bowel Syndrome, for 44 years. Her cellular level healing combined with dietary recommendations and at home reinforcement techniques brought me final and complete healing!" **C.L. Lillian, AL**

"Alice helped me during a difficult time especially with my diagnosis of osteoporosis. Her self-healing of breast cancer was a wonderful role model for me for my own healing. Alice's suggestions around diet and supplements gave me confidence in my process. My last scan showed that my bones had indeed improved. If you want to be inspired to heal, read this book." **B.M. Pensacola, FL**

"For several years, I had been dealing with the frustration and pain of Crohn's disease and sinus problems. Working with Alice gave me the relief that no doctors or medicines achieved. I am thrilled, as I do not have the pain of these health issues anymore. Best of all, I just feel better about myself." **K.D. San Diego, CA**

"I tried everything to help my kidney failure, but it continued to get worse. When I reached stage 4 kidney failure, I knew I had to try something else. Alice's approach to healing absolutely turned everything around. I am eternally grateful." **P.H. Freeport, FL**

"Two months after surgery removed my breast cancer, it started to grow back. I wanted a way to address the cause, not the symptom, and Alice's approach, which is explained in this book, gave me just that. She facilitated me to reach for the root cause within my subconscious and unconscious, and transform it. This work not only reversed the cancer growing back, but also healed two other health issues I was having. If you want complete healing this is the way to go!" **Y.S. Seagrove Beach, FL**

"Alice's 'Wellness Wisdom' approach helped me to successfully navigate multiple high dose chemotherapy treatments and two stem cell rescues for cancer. Each healing session we did brought dramatic results to my immune system, my body, and my spirit. Her experience with diet and healing foods, along with her spiritual insights helped me heal on multiple levels. I felt lighter and brighter after each session and my body reflected this shift. I felt totally supported, protected, and balanced in ways that are often dismissed in the medical community. Learning her 'whole' prescription for health and healing is a must for everyone." **A.P. Atlanta, GA**

"From debilitating migraines to obsessive fears to chronic health issues – Alice's work with me has transformed it all! And she has taught me how to heal myself. I recommend what is inside of this book for everyone!" **B.T. Holt, FL**

"My daughter had OCD, Obsessive Compulsive Disorder, for 12 years. I tried everything including many medications and counseling. I spent thousands of dollars, and nothing worked. My heart broke for my daughter who worried about death 95% of the time. I thank God for Alice and her healing approach. After two sessions, my daughter was transformed. Her OCD patterns have not returned." **J.D. Santa Rosa Beach, FL**

"My biggest learning from Alice's 'Wellness Wisdom' is that all healing is spiritual first. I have worked with several people in the healing arts, but Alice's approach is the most complete and effective. Together we healed several health and emotional issues that could not be addressed through traditional methods. More importantly, my spiritual awareness and growth has been incredible. I am grateful and recommend her approach to everyone!" **M.E. NYC, NY**

"Alice's 'Wellness Wisdom' has been a great resource to me. She looks at the bigger picture, not just one aspect of the healing. Her holistic recommendations together with her transformational healing helped me to heal many health issues and unwanted life patterns. The best part is that I now live joyfully in the present, with health and peace. P.S. I love the healing foods, cooking tips and holistic resources." **C.D. DeFuniak Springs, FL**

D1284155

About The Author

Alice McCall holds a BS in Psychology and an MBA. She is a certified Hypnotherapist, Reiki I & II practitioner and Quantum Touch practitioner. Ms McCall has a successful career in Transformational Energy Healing, Spiritual Counseling and Inspirational Speaking. Her passion is to help others heal using the entire mind, body, spirit, emotion spectrum. Her specialty is serious health issues and disease.

Her numerous articles are published in many national and local publications. Her internet radio program has been labeled "a breath of fresh air." She offers CDs, phone sessions, retreats, and educational workshops. Ms McCall lives in Santa Rosa Beach, Florida with her Yorkshire terrier, Keta. She is currently working on her next book.

Alice attributes all success from her practice to the healing presence of God.

www.healingpath.info

Cover art by Shannon Faulk-Vonderheide
Shannon lives in Defuniak Springs Florida with her husband James and a menagerie of animal friends. In addition to being an artist, she is a licensed Massage Therapist and Reiki Master.

The symbolism behind the cover art: The figure is standing in a traditional sun salutation stance projecting the energy of "Yes, thank you God, I healed myself." The heart symbolizes an open heart that can be seen and felt from every direction, spreading joy to all.

www.RedLotusCenter.com

Healing Path Presents

Wellness Wisdom

A Reference Book for Natural Health & Healing

Inspired by One Woman's Journey with Breast Cancer

Alice McCall

Healing Path Concepts

Disclaimer

*The information presented in this guide by **Healing Path** is intended for educational purposes only. These statements have not been evaluated by the FDA and are not intended to diagnose, cure, treat, or prevent disease. Before using any supplements, diets, protocols, or techniques it is always advisable to consult with your own health care provider. The intention of this reference guide is to share what Alice McCall learned while healing herself of breast cancer naturally, without traditional medical procedures. This information is from her best knowledge and first hand experience. It is to be used by readers at their own discretion.*

Published by Healing Path Concepts
755 Grand Blvd, #B 105-162
Miramar Beach, FL 32550

Printed in the United States of America
ISBN 978-0-578-02190-4

Acknowledgement

I want to thank those who supported me in taking the less traveled path of healing. Your positive support and faith in my journey was invaluable to my complete healing.

Healing From the Inside Out - *Alice*

Contents

Introduction

Your mind, body, and spirit have the ability to maintain health, prevent disease, and heal unwanted health and emotional issues.

With support from what you think, what you eat, and how much rest you allow yourself, your body can heal itself. By simply including your spiritual inner self in the process, you can live in alignment with your soul and your life's purpose.

Somehow, we have gotten off track from the basics of health and spirituality, and we get in our own way. We inhibit our body's ability to prevent disease by eating the wrong foods and by repeatedly spinning ourselves up with fear, anger, worries, and doubts.

In 2007, I healed myself of breast cancer, and other associated health issues. This occurred in less than four months without traditional medical methods. I achieved this by focusing on mastering my thoughts and emotions, feeding my body what it needed to heal and become whole, allowing myself to rest often and sleep long, and participating in a spiritual journey that was incredible.

I find that what I know through my practice as a spiritual energy healer, along with what I learned during my healing journey, is seldom known or utilized. Yet, so many people are seeking answers for their health and wholeness.

I decided to compile the wellness wisdom gained in my healing journey and put it all in one easy to use reference book. My goal is to share information that can help you prevent disease, stay healthy, and grow into a place of peace, contentment, and joy.

This reference book is packed full of information to support your body's ability to naturally heal and maintain health. Part of my mission with this book is to celebrate the variety of wellness tools that are available to us. Each one of these tools played a roll in my journey, but some were brief introductions into a modality and others were included in my daily routine. Don't feel like you should do everything in this book – it would unquestionably be too much. I simply hope to enable you to discover and use the healing approaches that appeal to you.

I want to emphasize that I focused on my top three healing priorities each day, and did the rest as I could. I share those priorities in this book and feel that they are the basics for maintaining health and healing. I also suggest changing your routine gradually, incorporating one aspect at a time. Trying to do too much at once can make for a stressful situation, which is not conducive to positive health.

My intention for sharing the information in this book is to offer hope for those who have serious diseases and ideas for those who want to prevent disease and maintain their health. It provides many opportunities for you to step onto your healing path, achieve what you desire, and obtain good health. This book contains detailed information learned through experience, research, and consulting with experts. I designed it to be an easy to use reference and an introduction to many forms of self-healing.

The information in this book was learned with love and is shared with love.

Alice

My Healing Journey

On July 9th 2007, I left the doctor's office at 4:00pm in a state of shock. I was told that I had cancer of the left breast - ductal carcinoma, estrogen and progesterone receptive. This was discovered with a mammogram and biopsy. The doctor wasn't warm or empathetic and injected me with a fair amount of fear. When I got home I just sat in my living room for several hours staring blankly at a wall, saying the mantra 'I am healed and whole' over and over. I couldn't think. I couldn't move.

I am a professional transformational energy healer. I work with the spiritual, mental, and emotional connection within the body. I have helped hundreds of people heal themselves of serious diseases, emotional issues, and unwanted life patterns. However, all this went out the door when I received the diagnosis. I was numb and in disbelief. "How could this happen to me, a healer?"

I now know the answer to my question. It was part of my life's journey to experience this and to learn from it, so I can help others. I consider the entire experience a gift. However, in those first days, that idea was not even on my radar screen.

If you are ever faced with a life threatening disease, make the conscious choice not to move into fear. I have talked with others who have experienced serious diseases and they all share the same wisdom in hindsight, "Do not make important decisions quickly, especially when you are in fear." I totally agree with them. If you do make hurried decisions, you may regret them. I know someone who was diagnosed with breast cancer and chose to remedy it through a mastectomy. She made this decision quickly while she was still in a state of shock and fear. She did not take the time to consider other options or consult with other physicians. When the breast tissue was brought to the lab, extensive testing showed that there was no cancer within it. She was minus a breast, and the surgery to reconstruct her breast was not performed well, leaving her in constant pain. Two more surgeries could not correct the damage done. She now lives with constant pain, filled with anger and distrust - the deep emotional scars of an unfortunate situation.

Always take the time for some deep breaths to allow yourself to think, feel, and assess a situation from your heart. Remember that nearly all important decisions can be postponed for a short while, and it is always your right to seek a second opinion.

From that very first day, I made the decision never to claim my diagnosis. I never said, "I have cancer." Since our thoughts and words create everything saying, "I have cancer," could help create it. Why tell your body that it has cancer? Your body takes commands from your mind and your thoughts. I always chose to say, "I was diagnosed with cancer." I focused on keeping my attitude positive. When I had one of my many down moments, I asked friends and colleagues for help, to listen, to pray, and to visualize my healing with me.

I also made the conscious decision to tell only those who I knew would be supportive of my self-healing journey, versus those who may bring fear and doubt into my process. Granted, they would do it out of a concern for me, but I could not have fear and doubt in my space. Healing occurs rapidly when you just know that it is so. There is no room for doubt.

I had enough doubt and fear of my own lingering at my back door, without other people's influence. Although I worked at mastering these emotions, in retrospect, what worked the best was getting out of my own way and just allowing life to present itself. When I started allowing, all flowed seamlessly to a successful conclusion. I was led to the right people and principles to help me and support me. I am blessed.

It was recommended that my left breast and lymph glands under my left arm be surgically removed, with radiation, chemotherapy and possible hormone treatments following the surgery. I chose another path – healing myself without medical intervention. Happily, all parts of my body are intact, healthy, and whole. This has been verified through tests done by both medical and holistic health professions.

My first healing focus was the spiritual, mental, and emotional cause of my diagnosed disease. All healing is spiritual first, then mental and emotional, and lastly physical. Thought and emotion create all. Negative thoughts and emotions can become buried in the cells of our bodies as dense, heavy energy. Over time, this dense energy can cause a breakdown within the body in the place where it is stored. To ensure healing the cause, it is important to identify what is buried in your cells and transform it. This is critical whether you embrace a traditional approach, a holistic approach, or a combination of the two. Without this work, it is easier for your health issue to return.

To combat my diagnosis I immediately started doing deep inner work at the subconscious and cellular levels to identify what was stored in my breast that needed to be released and transformed. It was amazing! As I did the work, day by day and week by week, I continually felt lighter, brighter, and happy, even though I was diagnosed with cancer. Within a couple of weeks, people who did not know about my condition would say to me, "You look great." If they knew about my condition, they said, "I cannot believe how happy and joyful you are." Everyone could feel the shift of my energy, as I did.

My second focus was diet and nutrition. Once freed of the density of your own buried negative thoughts and emotions, your body has the space to heal naturally. I wanted to totally support my body's ability to heal naturally, so I chose an alkaline, macrobiotic, organic diet. This diet is free of yeasty foods like wheat and cheese, free of sugar, spicy foods, caffeine, and alcohol. I lightly cooked most of my food and I included nutritional gifts, like seaweed. I drank pure spring water and healing herbal teas. I continued this diet throughout my healing journey and beyond it.

Why this approach? Yeast, sugar, and acid in your intestinal environment tend to foster disease – actually helping it grow. Putting toxins and hormones into your body from non-organic foods interferes with your body's ability to heal and maintain optimum health.

My diet consisted of 50-60% vegetables. The remainder included healthy grains such as millet, brown rice, and quinoa, along with protein primarily derived from fresh white flaked fish, salmon, and legumes. I ate very little fruit, since all fruit is full of natural sugars. Studies have shown that cancer may thrive with sugar, so I didn't want to take the chance and ate as little natural sugar as possible. Fruit like oranges and strawberries are also acidic which conflicts with an alkaline diet. I did eat blueberries, apples, pears, dried apricots, and raisins in moderation. These fruits' individual healing properties targeted a specific area that needed improvement.

My third priority was to get plenty of rest and sleep. Your body heals best while you are sleeping.

I used medical diagnostics (urine, bowel, saliva, blood, and gastro tests) to tell me what was going on inside of me. I learned what areas my body was deficient in, so I could address them with diet, supplements, other protocols, and additional energy work. Interestingly, I learned that I had parasites that were causing extreme diarrhea, discomfort, and exhaustion. My research uncovered several studies that link cancer to fungus or parasite problems. A big prevention tip is to change your intestinal environment to be more alkaline. It is much harder for fungus, disease, bacteria, or cancer to thrive in an alkaline environment. Also, add a probiotic supplement to your daily routine to raise the level of good bacteria in your stomach.

My journey became complicated not only by the addition of parasites, but also by dysplasia of the vagina, and a high metal toxicity. I now value all of these experiences as they caused me to look further and learn more, which I use to maintain my own health and to help others heal and prevent disease. Each aspect of my journey is shared in this book.

What else is important?

- Find tools that help you stay centered, focused and balanced throughout your journey. I used breath work, meditation, yoga, Pilates and Qigong on a regular basis. I also continued my daily walk with my dog.

- Look at other alternative health care practices. I chose acupuncture to support my body's ability to heal naturally. It was my treatment of choice.

- Consider slowing your use of unfermented soy products. There are documented health risks associated with these soy products, especially in relation to breast cancer.

- Include fermented soy products. I also added other fermented foods such as umeboshi plum and sauerkraut. Fermented foods are good for your stomach's balanced health. If you are trying to maintain your health or heal, your intestinal environment can help or hinder your success. Eighty percent of your immune system operates in your gut.

- Clear free flowing lymph (liquid) throughout your lymphatic system is critical to your body's health. I energetically transformed what was stored in my lymph glands that was unhealthy. I also added two lymph drainage supplements, self-massage, and jumping on a small trampoline five plus minutes a day. All of these facilitate lymph flowing easily and joyfully throughout your lymphatic system.

- Metals in our body detract from all aspects of health. Did you know that most commercial antiperspirants have aluminum in them? When we shave our underarms, it facilitates an immediate dump of aluminum into our underarm lymph glands. Free flowing lymph is needed for our immune system to work properly, so why clog it with aluminum? Other aluminum products like coated pans and aluminum foil should be avoided.

- Detoxification is critical. This includes detoxification of buried mental and emotional density, environmental toxins, radiology and other harmful medical procedures, and ingested hormones, antibiotics, and toxins. I included several foods and protocols for detoxification regularly, but in the end of my journey, I specifically engaged in metal detoxification.

- Use thermography for your medical screenings. It is a <u>very</u> early detector of cancer and it is healthy screening alternative, since it does not put harmful radiology into your body.

- Lessen your use of underwire bras. They cut off the circulation of your body's blood, lymph, and energy to your breast tissue.

- Use guided imagery to change what is happening in your body. I used it to visualize the shrinking of my lump in meditations.

- Watch fun movies that make you laugh. The vibration of laughter supports healing. It also helps maintain your health through boosting your immune system.

- Consider the use of homeopathy and/or vibrational protocols to support you body's healing.
- Minimize electromagnetic and geopathic stress in and around your home.
- Use spiritual drawing, journaling, and dreaming to help manifest your body's complete healing.

On Sunday, August 12, 2007, only five weeks into my journey, I felt a total energy shift in my tumor after a self-facilitated energy session. The lump in my breast felt dormant. However, I could not prove it until I learned about a thermogram scan. On Nov 2, 2007, I had a thermogram scan, which validated what I already knew – there was no longer any cancer in my breast.

Although this was a journey to heal my diagnosis of cancer, it became a spiritual journey for me. With each healing session, I gained a deeper connection with my inner self and became closer to my Creator, my angels, and my guides. Once cleansed of the density in my body, put there by buried negative emotions and thoughts, I was able to fill myself with lighter vibrating energy. Today I am just so happy. Nothing gets to me or bothers me. This is a huge gift, and I have the diagnosis of cancer to thank for it.

My Healing Priorities

Early in my journey, it became clear to me that I needed to focus on what was most important to my healing. I discovered so much that was important and could positively affect my journey, but there were only so many hours in each day.

I learned that taking the extra time during the day to sleep and rest, combined with the time it takes to shop, prepare, and cook healthy foods could take eight hours a day. If I did this, when would there be time for me to work, do yoga, Qigong, and my detoxification protocols, and watch movies that make me laugh?

Unfortunately, there was not enough time to do it all. I decided to focus on my top three priorities every day, and fill in with the rest of the wonderful support practices during the week/month when I could.

It is important to acknowledge that if you push yourself too hard to do everything, you could create stress for yourself, which will hinder your healing process. Everyone I know who has experienced a major health issue ends up honoring a few simple priorities that make up their formula for success. Below is a summary of what worked for me: my simple top three daily priorities and the other wonderful practices that I engaged in when I could. Each topic will be covered in this book in more detail.

Here are the Top Three Healing Priorities – I Focused on Them Daily

1. **Transformational Healing** to address the cause and to rework the body's energy into a healthy state (using the mind, emotion, and spiritual connection within the body). ***"You are what you think!"*** This is the first thing I focused on, and continued to focus on during my healing journey.
2. **Diet and Nutrition,** including foods and supplements that cleanse what is unhealthy inside your body. ***"You are what you eat!"*** It is a priority to prepare and cook healthy foods. My body was screaming for support, and I wanted to provide it.
3. **Sleep and Rest.** ***"Your body heals and renews while sleeping!"*** Without this priority, it is likely that I would still be sick. I had to work at allowing myself to take the time to sleep and rest. We are so conditioned to push, push, push.

Other Approaches I Used to Support My Healing Journey

I incorporated these weekly, or as often as I could. They supported my healing and I believe in them.

1. **Positive Support.** I created an environment for complete healing both outside and inside of myself. Surround yourself with positive (non-fearful) people. Ask for help. Hold onto positive thoughts and emotions. Trust your journey and God. Laugh often. Watch movies that make you laugh. Never claim

your illness. Use imagery and positive affirmations to help manifest your healing. Set your intention – all follows intention. Use spiritual drawing, journaling, and dreaming to support your healing.

2. **Alternative Medical Support - Acupuncture.** I had acupuncture every one-two weeks to help tone, align, and support my body's natural healing. This was my treatment of choice.

3. **Medical Diagnostics.** I learned what was deficient in my body, so I could heal it spiritually, mentally, and through diet, supplements, and detoxification. Medical diagnostics were an invaluable tool.

4. **Cleansing & Detoxification** to release harmful toxins from environmental pollution, insecticides, and unwanted hormones, while enhancing the immune system's ability to do its job.

5. **Practices that Center, Balance, Oxygenate, & More.** I chose a combination of yoga, Pilates, Qigong, meditation, breath work, and walking, to keep me centered, balanced, oxygenated, healthy and in touch with my inner self. Choose the combination that invigorates you.

6. **Maintain a Healthy Stomach & Lymphatic System**. Eighty percent of the immune system lives in the gut. Sluggish lymph hinders immune system performance.

7. **Support from the Healing Arts**: Kinesiology, Reiki, and Massage.

8. **Screening Tools - Thermogram.** An early detector of cancer that does not use radiation. Radiation may cause potential cancer to grow.

9. **Alternative Support Remedies:** vibrational, homeopathic, herbal, and essential oils to help the body align with the spiritual and mental changes you create over the course of the healing journey.

10. **Minimize Electromagnetic & Geopathic Stress** inside and around your home.

11. **Other Preventative & Healing Practices.** Use non-aluminum deodorant, limit use of underwire bras, eliminate metals in your body, read the ingredients in your sunscreens, and don't re-biopsy.

Even though I like to have a plan, it all worked best when I approached the above practices (after the top three) organically. One day it felt right to start my day with Qigong, on another a walk on the beach with my dog. Some things do require planning like booking my appointments for acupuncture, which was ideally weekly but sometimes it was every two weeks. I ultimately approached my food and supplements the same way.

Today, I ask the rising sun each morning to tell me the energy for the day. Once aligned with that – all flows much better. Also, intention is huge, as all follows intention. Set the intention that you will be guided to know what practices and protocols to engage in each day. As a rule of thumb, if you are able to incorporate a few times a week one to three of the above areas, in addition to the top three priorities, you are doing well. As you read though this book, consider your priorities. Make a conscious choice to select a few things that are manageable to your life and will have a big impact on your health. Explore the remainder of alternative practices and ideas as they speak to you.

I got frustrated when people who had gone through successful healings would say, "Just relax and enjoy the process." At first, I wanted to make sure that I was doing everything that I knew was important. However, as I journeyed, I realized they were right. I had lots of help, and so do you. When I forgot something important, one of my angels would let me know. I finally fully turned over the reins to God, trusted the process, and yes, enjoyed the journey. I have totally embraced this as a way to live my life each day, and I would not change it for the world.

The Mind, Body, Spirit Connection

There is a spiritual, mental, and emotional connection to healing and maintaining health. This has been the founding principle of both my healing practice and my health journey.

You might be interested in discovering that the definition of healing in the dictionary is, 'to become whole,' not to fix what is broken. If you consider the wholeness of you, the way that God made you, it includes your mind, your emotions, your spirit, and your body. Being whole involves having all parts of you aligned and operating from the same program – the program of your higher soul self. This is a powerful way for you to be linked with your spiritual purpose and agreements for this lifetime.

It is so fascinating that most of the medical community, whether traditional or alternative, focuses nearly exclusively on the physical body. Some say they are mind body spirit healers – but they do not work with the layers of mind - the subconscious, unconscious, and conscious. There are also those that do not work with emotions or connect to the spiritual lesson involved with ill health and disease.

True healers know that all parts have to be involved to be healed wholly – to prevent the health issue from returning. This works best when it occurs within one's own mind, body, spirit, and emotion network. True healers have an understanding that powerful spiritual lessons occur during the healing process, and they are minimized if the individual is not included in their healing process. Practitioners who move energy around for someone else do have a healing impact, but it can be fleeting since the person is putting back the thought patterns or emotions that initially caused the illness.

Healing occurs at a spiritual level first, the mental and emotional levels are second, and then it manifests physically. That is why this was my first step, my first priority, in my self-healing journey.

All Healing is Spiritual First

The most important aspect of healing is to know from deep inside of you that you are healed, coupled with the total trust of your process as it unfolds. Healers understand that this deeply held knowing is significant enough to move mountains, and change the cells in your body.

I am a spiritual, transformational energy healer. I have no doubt that when God sends me someone to help, that I can. I know without a doubt that you can heal any issue, if you believe it to be so, if you do the work of shifting the negative energy within you (at both the cellular/body levels and at the emotional/subconscious levels), and if you trust own inner wisdom and intuition. This means listening to and following your heart and soul.

Because healing occurs within your own mind, body, spirit, and emotion connection, it is incredibly important to have a deep-seated belief in the process and to have a personal and trusting relationship with your Creator. It is important to spend silent sacred meditation time with God and your angels, to receive their guidance, their assistance, and their spiritual healing support.

This section includes a summary of ideas to help you stay in the place of optimistic trust. Know that the suggestions included are important, even if they don't always seem to be. These principles have helped many in my healing practice. They are what I used to keep me on the path when I went into fear and doubt. Also in this section are a couple of spiritual healing experiences that I received while on my journey.

In the end, this spiritual connection with you, God, your angelic helpers becomes more important and more profound than the physical healing. It transcends all. It fills you, lightens you, and expands you totally. It is so profound that you will never go back to life as it was before. It is so important that you will thank God for your gift of illness, as I did.

Ideas to Stay in Optimistic Trust & Belief

Let's start from the beginning. From the day I left the doctor's office, I never claimed my diagnosis. I never said, "I have cancer." We know that thoughts and emotions create all. We also know that your body takes commands from your thoughts and words. If I had said, "I have cancer," that would have created what I did not want. It could actually tell my body to create more of the disease. I choose to say that I was "diagnosed with cancer," as that is not claiming it.

Two years earlier, I worked successfully with a 43-year-old woman who was diagnosed with stage 3 lymphoma. It was labeled as non-curable. When she first started talking to me she said, "I have stage 3 lymphoma, and it is incurable. I guess I will have to shave my head and wear a baseball cap."

I said, "Do not go there! You are envisioning what you do not want to happen." I taught her to say that she was diagnosed with lymphoma and to envision what she wanted. Never claim your disease and always envision what you want.

All follows your intention. She told me that she did not want chemotherapy and radiology because of the awful side effects. She wanted to heal naturally. However, she was recommended to start her procedures within three weeks. Together we set the intention that she would have all the time that she needed to heal her body naturally. Two weeks later, her Mom miraculously called and shared that she found a lymphoma specialist and encouraged her to get a second opinion.

The new Doctor concurred that her case was very bad, but he also told her that he had seen worse. He recommended saving the silver bullet of chemotherapy and radiology for last, instead of using it first. He even recommended waiting three months for a return visit and suggested re-running the tests at that time. She chose his recommendation versus her previous Doctor's approach of immediate treatment. This choice, which had a medical doctor's backing, gave her the safe haven to wait and do her own work. He did not give her anything to take or do during this time. He did give us the opening we needed to effect her healing, which she did successfully, without medical treatments. So set your intentions.

It was the same for me when I set the following intention with faith and trust: *"I will be guided and supported to heal myself successfully, so I can offer hope for others, and share what I learn."*

The following are my affirmations from a journal entry dated July 10th, 2007, the day after I was told that I had cancer. The drawing below is a visual interpretation of those positive phrases, which I drew the following day.

'I am healed and whole. I have never believed that I have cancer. It is not a possibility for me. My mind is strong in that area. The thing they called cancer was a fleeting gift to allow me to uplift my attitude and lifestlye. It came from nothing and it will return to nothing. I am healed and whole healthy left breast. I am healed whole healthy body. It is just how it is. I love myself. I enjoy my journey.'

I focused on keeping my attitude positive. I acted as if I was well, and I thought as if I was well. I did my affirmations and thanked God for my healing. Despite what was going on and how I felt, I knew this was incredibly important to do, since your mind creates all, and your body takes commands from your mind and thoughts.

I would touch my lump each day and when I felt its presence, I'd say, "The tissue and cells in my breast are healthy and normal. All obstructions or tumors in my ducts are gone. I am healthy breast." I was not saying what I felt with my fingers. Rather, I used my thoughts and words to create what I wanted. Remembering this still brings tears to my eyes.

Use your thoughts and words to create your healing. This powerful tool is always available to you. This is another tip for healing, maintaining health, preventing disease, and amplifying your manifestation work: become a master of your thoughts. Learn to focus on the positives and what you want your life to be. Proactively use positive affirmations to envision what you want to happen in a situation. If you go to a place of fear, worry, judgment, doubt, anger, or sadness, acknowledge it. Then shift anything negative so that you are aware of the positive. Always reach for the higher thought. For example, if your thought is, "I am worried that this approach does not work," reach for, "My healing path works successfully." Then you can reach for the positive thought that, "I am joyful, as I am healed and whole."

I bought fun movies that made me laugh, which helped me hold onto an energy vibration that supports healing. I would put on happy music and sometimes I would dance to it. These may seem like little things, but they are huge. When you hold onto laughter and joy, it speeds your healing. In addition, this vibration supports manifestation of any kind. Good reasons to smile and laugh often.

When I had one of my many down moments, I asked friends and colleagues to help, to listen, to pray, and to visualize my healing. Always ask for help. I am a successful transformational healer – but I asked for help and support. So many want to help but do not know how. Even if your request is simply to ask, "Can I vent to you tonight? I just need someone to talk to." Honor yourself and ask for help.

I want to share one word of caution. Carefully choose who you share your health issue with, if you decide to embark on something that is non-traditional or partially non-traditional. Why? The majority of the world lives in fear. You do not want anyone making you second-guess what you are doing. You must step out with total faith and trust. Healing occurs quickly when you have the knowing that it is so. There is no room for doubt.

If people put fear into you, you could begin to second-guess yourself. In addition, if a lot of people know about your health issue, they will think they are helping by calling you every day or two and checking up on you, and asking for a report. If you spend everyday repeating the details of your health issue, you will have less time to heal, and to have silence and peace. What is worse is that you could be creating your health issue's reality by constantly discussing it. Surround yourself with positive, supportive people. Stay away from those who inject fear and doubt into you.

I chose to keep my health issue within a small circle of friends and colleagues that I felt would support me in my choice. Initially this only included one family member.

About two months earlier, I was told I had dysplasia in my vagina – level 3. These are displaced cells, which if they stay in place could turn into cancer. At the same time, I was diagnosed with a serious virus of the cervix. I was told that it would always be part of my profile and that it would never go away. I chose to use my healing approach, healing the buried mental/emotional cause of the issue. I did my own work along with phone assistance from a practitioner who understands the medicine of herbs and heals using a shamanic perspective, which is similar to mine. This perspective means all disease or unwanted patterns simply come from two areas: (1) Either something is within you that should not be there, coming primarily from our own buried negative thoughts and emotions or (2) there is something missing that should be there – like a part of us that we repressed or left behind.

During this time most of my family was not supportive of my approach and wanted me to have surgery. Their communications were anxious and fearful. I knew they were coming from a place of love and concern, but I knew it would escalate if they learned of my diagnosis of breast cancer. Therefore, I chose to shield myself from their fearful reaction.

I am sharing this because we always have choices. We do not have to tell everyone everything no matter what the topic is – health or otherwise. I always feel a good barometer is to include those that support and enhance your energy and bypass those that deplete it, especially through fear and doubt. I could not have any fear or doubt in my space during my healing journey. It takes time to recover from a fearful interaction with someone, even if it is well meaning. I chose to use that time to focus on healing myself instead.

By the way, after six weeks I went for a second opinion regarding the dysplasia. The size of the displaced cells was 50% reduced and the biopsy came back at level 0, when it had been at level 3. The doctor agreed with my request to wait a few months since I was moving in the right direction. Ten months later, I had my annual GYN exam and a pap test was taken of both the cervix and the vagina. Both results reported normal, with no sign of the virus that I was told would forever be a part of me. This health issue resolved itself by utilizing two things – the spiritual, mental, and emotional healing of the cause, and the use of specific herbs (some used as a tea and some used as a douche), which supported my body to heal naturally.

Address the Cause:
Your Buried Negative Thoughts & Emotions

I effected change in my lump within five weeks of my healing journey. I felt the energy of the lump change to a state of dormancy. This was verified by several practitioners that do body testing or kinesiology readings. *(Unfortunately, I could not prove it with traditional standards, until nearly three months later when I learned about thermograms.)*

How did this happen? It happened by addressing the cause, not the symptom, of my health issue.

The cause of all disease, ill health, emotional issues, and unwanted life patterns is a buried negative thought or emotion. I have mentioned before how your thoughts and emotions are your creative force. This is how God made you. Your thoughts and emotions create your experiences, what you attract to yourself, how you feel, and your health issues.

When you hold onto a negative thought or emotion, it becomes buried in the cells of your body. It is held there as heavy, dense, dark, negative energy. Over time, this density can cause a malfunction in the part of the body where it resides. Your thoughts from early years, including from the womb, are so deep that they may form into a subconscious memory and automatic subconscious patterns. This can create the same energy repeatedly within you, without you having conscious awareness of what is happening.

Nearly everything that is used medically and holistically addresses symptoms and works solely with the physical body. Sometimes other approaches identify the cause, but do not work towards transforming it, or do not transform it at both the cellular and subconscious levels. Some people clear the core issue but do not give the subconscious a new habit way of being, to replace the old way that was there for so long. This can create a big opening for the old pattern to return, and the health issue along with it. All of these elements are an essential part of a total and complete healing – returning to wholeness.

Transforming and healing the buried thought, emotion, and the associated dense energy, allows your body the freedom to heal naturally. It also replaces the automatic subconscious pattern, so it does not continue to recreate the cause.

Because of my background as an energy healer, immediately after the diagnosis I started doing healing work at the subconscious, unconscious, and cellular levels. The first goal was identifying what was stored in my breast that needed to be transformed. This is the most important part of healing. It is also the most important tool for maintaining health and creating the life you desire.

The cause is rooted within your own mind, spirit, emotion, and body system. It may be so deep that you have no knowledge of it, like wounds from the womb, a traumatic birth, or even a past life. It is also linked to what your soul signed up to address and master in this lifetime.

Cellular transformational healing is an amazing experience. As I did this healing work on myself, I felt lighter, brighter, and happier even though I was diagnosed with cancer. People who did not know of my diagnosis would say, "You look great." If they did know, they commented, "How can you be so happy and joyful?" They could feel the shift in my energy, as I did. Within one week of sharing my diagnosis with a friend, we ran into each other and she said, "The clarity of your energy is amazing. I can see a huge difference. I am no longer concerned."

As I continued with sessions focusing on the emotional and mental causes, it became obvious that I was on a spiritual journey. I became lighter and brighter after each healing session, and I realized that without this gift called cancer, I would never have done the deep work to rid myself of my unconscious patterns. There was no logical reason to do it. I thought I had already cleared out all of my density nine years earlier when I healed myself of a lifetime of debilitating allergies, vertigo, chronic sinus infections, and intestinal infections.

I worked long and hard healing these lifelong issues nine years ago. None of the symptoms returned, despite living in the same environment that 'caused' them. This work was how I learned the basics of my healing practice, which is a combination of spiritual, psychological, and energy techniques. I have a degree in Psychology and am a certified Hypnotherapist, but I was guided on how to combine those techniques with energy formatting and assistance from the spirit realm.

At that time, however, I did not yet know about going to the womb or to past lives to clear possible connections to this lifetime. Eighty percent of the work in my breast cancer journey was related to past lives and spiritual lessons that my soul signed up to learn and master in this lifetime. The other 20% was subtle connections from this lifetime, including an experience in the womb.

Not everyone has past life connections that need to be cleared, but there could be underlying family tree issues or DNA issues that need to be addressed. For instance, I had a few issues that were passed to me from my Mom that I needed to address and clear. Each person's experience is different. I also believe that we all have what I call soul assignments. These often show up as health issues, emotional issues, or unwanted life patterns, but they are important to tackle in this lifetime.

Some of the causes that I discovered and transformed in relation to the breast cancer diagnosis were:

- A lack of emotional nourishment from others, including myself. Although over my lifetime I evolved to be someone that maintains a healthy lifestyle including time for meditation and personal interests, the subtle nuance was that I tended to be critical of myself, and pushed myself. I was not always gentle and compassionate with me.
- Patterns of abuse. Spiritually our life tends to mirror what we need to know or learn. In the first few weeks of my healing journey, three strangers treated me in a verbally abusive and disrespectful manner. I did not even know them. After the third incident, I finally got it. "Maybe," I thought, "this is showing up to tell me about something I am holding onto inside. Maybe it has something to do with my healing!" When I did the work, I was surprised to find many past lives of physical abuse where I was left feeling disrespected and not worthy. I brought this energy into this lifetime, and I realized it did create abusive relationships around me. Abuse can take many forms and upon reflection, I have been in relationships where men tried to take advantage of me, manipulate me, and generally not treat me with respect.

Remember what you hold onto inside of you is what you will get outside of you, even when the thought or emotion is unconscious or subconscious. I was holding onto the unconscious/subconscious thought that I was not respected and not worthy. This thought created life experiences that brought me to those who treated me with disrespect.

- <u>Feelings of betrayal</u> from a past life as a naval captain, a negative experience in the womb, and a memory from another lifetime of an arrow going into my breast from someone I trusted. The most interesting piece is that the arrow's location was exactly where my tumor resided. I asked Archangel Michael to remove the arrow, to affect the healing
- <u>Inner child work</u> from ages 3, 7, and 16, where I developed a sense of having to be responsible. These years set up a pattern of not letting the joyful child/woman surface and express herself freely.

I transmuted these causes, changing the dense energy into light positive energy through all parts of me. I did this primarily with the help from violet energy, forgiveness, and guided imagery. I made sure to clear the associated density in the cells of my body – primarily in my breast. I worked with my subconscious to heal any childhood or past life wounds and to replace ego's habit way of thinking and being with a more positive way to think and be. This freed up my body to heal naturally. I then supported my healing with direct energy work throughout my body, my immune system, and any other area that needed a boost.

Working Energetically on the Body & Within the Body

As my journey continued, I more actively engaged in energetic bodywork. This was directly aimed at helping my body catch up with the rapid spiritual, mental, and emotional growth that I was experiencing. There was a lag and since my body was stuck in a habit way of operating it took a while to fully integrate.

Spiritually I was vibrating at very high level, but my body was still in the lower vibration, causing the physical manifestation to lag.

Here is a visual from my direct bodywork done while in deep meditation.

With the help of my angels and guides, we cut off the supply chain so the tumor would no longer be able to flourish.

Later, I asked the attendees of my weekly guided meditation to join me in a visualization that reinforced the bodywork.

If a picture is worth a thousand words, what is true about words being a powerful creative force in our lives is also true for guided imagery. When many are imagining the same thing, at the same time, it amplifies the energetic force. Visualize what you want to occur and ask others to join you. Together feel the feelings as if it is already occurring. Feeling as if it is already occurring helps to bring your work into the present.

* Supply chain for tumor is cut off leaving it to wither + die off
* Sending it to the Light to find it's place of belonging

8/1/07

Another great guided imagery exercise that I used to effect change in my body was the classic Pac-Man visualization. I focused on seeing several Pac-Mans gobble up the tumor. In addition, the simplicity of visualizing my lump getting smaller and smaller until it was shrinking to nothing was also very effective. It gave specific commands to my body. Guided imagery shows your body what you want to have happen.

You can also use guided visualization to create the outcome you want. I worked with one of my clients who had a life threatening disease to visualize receiving positive news from her doctor when she went in for her three-month check up. We focused on how hearing the news felt good and the positive emotions that followed. This person returned from her check-up and reported that it happened exactly like we visualized, including who delivered the report, how he entered the room, and what he said.

There are other ways to work directly with your body. One day, I energetically sat with the tumor and asked it, "Why are you still here? What do you need to leave?" It told me, "Love."

I did transformational energy healing directly on my immune system and all of its components to make sure they were clear of density and were healthy. This included making sure my army of white blood cells was fully present in all divisions. I wanted to make sure that my body was functioning at its highest level so it could easily focus on healing itself.

When I found out that I had parasites, I did a different form of bodywork. In a meditative state, I went inside my intestines with the request, "Show me what you look like now." I saw a bunch of wild animals whose bodies were very small, but their heads were large. All of them were gazing at me with their eyes bulging and their teeth showing. It really elicited a fear response within me. I did not want to stay there, but I knew these angry animals represented the parasites. So, I took a deep breath in and out to calm me, I then asked my intestines, "Show me how you look healed and whole." What I received was the pure element of water moving through with gentle force. As the water flowed, the animals started to cling to the intestinal wall (which is what parasites do). The water kept flowing and washing until all the animals were gone.

Then the water quieted down. Beautiful pure white underwater plants started sprouting up everywhere, until they filled my entire intestines. I knew this was good bacteria. When I came out of this very deep and long session, the long-standing cramps in my stomach caused by the parasites were gone, and never returned.

No Room for
Bad Bacteria
Fungus, or Parasites!
only Good Flora!
9/21/07

Keep Your Chakras Clear & Healthy

Maintaining clear and healthy chakras is important for maintaining health and an effective immune system, but it is even more critical while healing. Why?

Chakras are energy centers within your body that constantly radiate and receive energy. When you hold onto negative thoughts or emotions, they are absorbed by your chakras. When this happens, your chakras stop functioning properly. Chakras are designed to be open and clear, allowing the energy of the Divine to flow freely through you. Buried negativity is dense and obstructs the flow within your chakras. It can also shrink or swell them depending on the negative emotion stored. Sluggish obstructed chakras have a negative effect on your immune system, something you do not want, especially during healing. Because each chakra radiates energy, it can also affect the surrounding parts of the body with the energy it is holding. If you are holding onto the energy of betrayal in your heart chakra, for instance, it can negatively affect the health of your heart or breasts.

There are many chakras in your body, but spiritual counselors and healers tend to focus on the seven primary ones. They are located deep in the center of your body between your tailbone and the crown of your head. Each is located near one of your glands. They push vital life force through your body to ensure vitality, health, and well-being. If you do not work on your chakras regularly you could experience: sluggishness, a lack of motivation, a sense of heaviness, a dulling of your mental abilities, a pattern of illness, or difficulty in accessing your spiritual self and higher purpose.

As a healer who is exposed daily to other people's energy it was even more important for me to be committed to a regular practice of cleansing, balancing, and tuning my energy centers. To make it easy on myself, I simply used my own CD, "Healthy Energy" to guide me. This offered me a daily 20-minute routine to ground, center, balance, and align my energy, along with a 45-minute weekly routine for cleaning and tuning my chakras. I still use this CD today to assist me in maintaining healthy energy in my body and chakras.

For those who are not healing, this practice remains important for many reasons. Clear and healthy chakras help to maintain an optimum functioning immune system, a good overall energy level within your body, and a boost to your creativity, wisdom, knowing, and intuition.

With our environment becoming so filled with stress and fear, many feel that you should do chakra work more frequently than weekly. Whether you work with your chakras weekly, monthly or annually, I recommend an initial deep and thorough cleansing, followed by a regular maintenance routine that works for you.

Spiritual Healing Support

I will admit that at times I became frustrated that there was a lot to work on, but my soul signed me up to master all of this gracefully and with trust. It included: healing multiple serious health issues (breast cancer, dysplasia of vagina, parasites, and heavy metal toxins), maneuvering the total financial downfall from real estate (I went through five foreclosures during this period), and not being able to work for several months. I was forced to live in total trust of provision. I had no choice. I was exhausted and ill from the parasites. This experience provided me with even more conviction to be able to help others, as I did go through all of it gracefully, with a calm center, and I was provided for. Somehow, I had the money to pay for my main living expenses.

Every time I got discouraged, I would say to myself, "If my soul/higher self thought I could do this, then I can do it." This thought really helped me to persevere. Remember that you are on your soul's journey. Know that you will succeed.

I received several new guides to help me during my healing journey, including my father, and his mother and father; all are deceased. During the early part of healing and transforming memories and patterns from the past, I received a Cobra animal guide in meditation.

This is from my journaling of that deep meditation.

Cobra is inside of my body. *"Wow, the tension is still there. Wow, what a build up.*

"Do not take this the wrong way. This is more than this lifetime – and then some. You know this."

(I do)

"You have in your own way been working on this for a long time!"

(Thank you for acknowledging it. I felt like maybe I didn't do a good enough job.)

"We acknowledge your work, but this is much more."

(Now what?)

"I am macho chi. I am the one who can punch it out."

(Thank you. What do I need to do?)

"You put up an energetic barrier by saying. 'What can I do'!"

(Ok. So, now what?)

"Allow me to go through you. You do not know my power. I am serpent. I hold nothing back. I am your protector, as well as your healer. Do you not understand that is what you need – both? I can keep other energies at bay while you heal inside. That is what you need."

(Yes I agree; I do need both)

"The lesson is I love you. You need to know that I/we love you. You are doing good work. You do it tirelessly, taking no time for yourself. You are driven by your passion - always helping others."

(Yes)

"We love you. We inspire you to let the healing waters flow though you. Open and allow. Absorb and integrate. But first, open and allow. You have done so much, as you had to take care of yourself. It is time to let go and let us, all of your helpers and guides, do for you. We love you. It will be okay."

The message from this animal guide held many things. Clearly, it included learning to be: 'Open and allow your healing to occur. You do not have to do it all yourself.' I needed this message. It helped me to relax and allow the process to occur.

True healers want to work with your mind, spirit, and emotion connections to your body. They understand that true and complete healing comes from your understanding, change, and integration of your own issues. They want to facilitate your conscious, unconscious, subconscious, and superconscious to become whole.

Someone else cannot have an experience for you, like the one I just shared. You can only have this by going within yourself, and it is awesome. Most people do not have the ability to facilitate this for themselves. There are practitioners, like myself, who can facilitate spiritual and healing experiences by helping you reach the deepest levels of yourself. I believe that the only true path to healing - total complete healing - is to go inside yourself and heal you. It has been this way for centuries, and it will always be this way. This was the path and the work that I did to heal myself.

At this point, I want to reinforce that there is always a gift inside of the apparent negative. My gift, the diagnosis of cancer, instigated me to do what my soul wanted. My soul wanted to remove all density so I could vibrate at the highest levels, achieving natural joy and approaching heaven on earth in this lifetime. I am just happy all the time now; not too much gets to me anymore. The joy and bliss that occurs when you transform yourself are exquisite, perfect, and whole. This gift is huge!

However, this gift is only there if you acknowledge that all things that seem negative have a gift inside.

Interspersed in the shifting and clearing of old memories, negative thoughts, past lives, and dense energy in my cells, I had beautiful spiritual and energetic healings such as this one. This occurred twelve days into my journey while in a meditative state.

I am on the beach. It is night; the moon is high in the sky. It's silver light, lights up the world here. The surf rolls in and out. "Why am I here?" I ask.

I am here for rework — for my final healing. I am alone, but I am not alone. I know my spirits and guides are around me. I walk into the cleansing salt water. My robe of white gauze easily allows the water to reach my skin. The salt of the sea is absorbed by my body, bringing a cleansing that is so natural and so perfect that all fear within me melts away. I stand letting the surf swirl around me - in and out. The rhythm is balancing. It is hypnotic. My being and my body are being purged of all impurities. All negativity and all foreign substances like viruses, bacteria, tumors, displaced cells, and cysts. As I stand here, I know deep inside of my heart that I am truly and finally healed. The nodule in my left breast is gone. I see it. I know it. The displaced cells in my vagina are gone. All parts of my body are perfect, whole, aligned and in right order.

Alice's Healing 7/21/07

Archangel Michael and St. Germaine are with me - one on each side of me. They carry me out further, so I can be totally immersed. They lovingly hold my body. As I am righted again on my feet, Michael scoops out the nodule in my breast, and Germaine loosens and releases the remaining old cells in my vagina that were once called a lesion. Both tell the virus in my cervix to go. Both surround me with love, peace, and joy.

I am carried to the beach where a chair awaits me and I am wrapped in a dry blanket. I am heavy. I nod off to another place knowing that I am protected. The place is to my future.

This visual is what creatively came out of me, after the work was done.

I had many spiritual/energetic experiences during my healing journey. I still get emotional when I remember them because I had such awesome support from my angels, guides, and deceased family members. An added benefit of these experiences is that they gave me a perspective and a confidence that helped me to persevere, despite my human emotions. How could you not doubt success with experiences such as these?

One of my clients with a serious disease told me that she was so changed from our work together that it was unbelievable. Her attitude, perspective, and all the pieces of her were now much more positive. She also shared that the result of her journey didn't matter because she would always be grateful to have had this experience and growth. She said, "I would not change my healing journey for the world."

Some time in the first two months of my journey, I was told in a meditation that I was healed and that the tumor would physically leave when I had learned all that I was suppose to learn. I asked, "Who is telling me this?" I was told that it was St. Germaine. I was very happy, as I knew I could trust Germaine, my faithful healing partner.

My journey took a while, since I had a lot to learn. Although the thermogram showed no cancer on October 4, 2007, the lump did not completely go away until the following April. During that time, I also had parasites and metal toxicity that allowed me the opportunity to learn more about all aspects of healing – body, mind, and spirit.

Summary: Healing with Mind, Body, Spirit, & Emotion

Healing can be a long and winding road or a straightforward march to the finish line. Regardless of what the path looks like, I have found that including the following work helps to ensure a complete and successful healing. Here is a summary of what I did in each category.

1. **Healing the mental/emotional causes.** I reached deep within me to learn the mental and emotional buried causes of my health issue. I worked to transform them and replace them with healthier energy. I set intentions for my work and asked my spiritual helpers, light energy, and universal elements for assistance. As I directed the healing work, I would ask them to carry out certain tasks to aid in the healing process. I did this work within the subconscious and unconscious parts of me, along with requesting guidance from my higher superconcious self. This work was the most critical as it addressed the cause.
2. **Receiving spiritual healing within meditation.** I held the space, going to a deep meditative place in order to receive this type of healing support. I did not direct this work, but rather set the intention and allowed it to occur. All of my healing experiences during my journey were amazing, but these were the most poignant, as they showed me just how much I was taken care of. As a result, I felt loved and I knew that I could not fail.
3. **Conducting energy work directly on my body and its components.** I directed this work at the subconscious and unconscious levels. It included cleansing and renewing my body's organs and immune system. Guided imagery was a part of this work, as it showed my body what I wanted to have happen.
4. **Allowing my body to energetically transform itself.** In this work, which was done at the cellular level, I allowed my body to heal itself. I did this by asking a particular part of my body what it needed to be healed and whole. The most profound work in this category occurred when I simply asked different parts of my body to show me what they looked like when they are healed and whole. I then held that vision and thanked my body for achieving it.
5. **Maintaining a healthy energy flow in my body.** I worked on my chakras in a meditation using light energy and angels. I used my own CD, 'Healthy Energy', to guide me in this practice weekly. I always feel better after I work on my chakras.

I find that the above work goes more smoothly when #1 is completed first. The reason is that as long as any negative density remains within you, it is difficult for the body to fully heal.

I always do my work within the sacred circle, which establishes a sacred space. I utilize a deep regressed or meditative state to fully affect all the parts of me, or my clients. All of the aspects of my work offered incredible experiences that I am honored to have gone through. This created my healing without drugs and procedures that have harmful side effects.

For 80% of the mind, body, spirit, and emotion healing, I was both the directing healing practitioner and the patient. I am grateful that 20% was supported by fellow healers. They allowed me to step more fully into the role of the patient while they directed and supported the work being done. I want to emphasize that it is important to reach out for help. Having their support was invaluable to me.

For me, my journey reinforced the reality that once you are on the healing path, your higher self and soul wants all of your density, buried thoughts, and buried emotions gone. Spiritually we are all called upon to continuously evolve, working towards vibrating at a higher level. Often, when I am working with a client on an issue many other issues show up so they can be cleared and resolved at the same time. It is all good. It means that your soul wants you to be crystal clear.

I counsel my clients to not become discouraged, and to be thankful when their spiritual helpers present them with physical signals that there is more to heal. For example, if you start to have a chronic neck problem while working on high blood pressure, it could be a signal that there is something else within you that needs to be transformed.

I realize that this is a new way of thinking, but please be open to the possibility. Being alert to these signals and healing them could ward off serious health issues, disease, and unwanted patterns. This way of thinking and being can also fuel the evolution of your soul, which means embracing a calmer, healthier way of being.

In addition to the intensive spiritual, mental emotional healing described, I also received occasional Reiki support, and intermittent psychic and meditation support from several colleagues. Each gave me invaluable information that helped in my journey, and some helped though distance healing. Their confidence in the success of my journey, especially in the beginning, really bolstered me.

My continued gratitude also goes to my creator, God, the source of all, to my healing partners: Archangel Michael, the Ascended Master St. Germaine, Archangel Raphael, Kuan Yin, Mother Earth, the element of water, and all of my wonderful animal guides and healing guides. Special appreciation also goes to my father and my grandmother (his mom), both deceased, for their ongoing active support of my healing.

I want to acknowledge my healing partner and beloved pet, Keta. Besides grounding me for my own healing work, she gave me constant and dedicated support throughout my journey.

Before I end this section, I want to reiterate that the most important part of healing and maintaining health is to do the emotional and mental work. Clients come to me with emotional issues they want addressed like constant anger, or feeling stuck, without being aware of how tackling these issues in their beginning stages is a powerful health prevention tool. The beauty is that this work not only heals the issue they came to address, but also prevents an associated health issue from manifesting in the body.

If you are healing, remember that your health issue could come back or stay as a chronic condition if this work is not completed. I have worked with several clients who have experienced returning health issues after medical procedures. Here is just one example.

I received a call from a woman and she told me that she had undergone breast cancer surgery two months earlier, and that it was starting to grow back. She indicated that she did not want to go the traditional route again. She asked if I could help, and I said yes.

Using my spiritual transformational energy healing approach, we effected change at the subconscious and the cellular levels to remove the emotional and mental root cause of the cancer. The root cause was linked with feelings of shame. I know through experience that this emotional energy also becomes buried in the kidneys and the thyroid gland, so I facilitated the transformational work in those areas, as well as the breast. We also cleansed the three related chakras: heart chakra (breast), sacral chakra (kidney), and throat chakra (thyroid), along with the corresponding areas of her back/spine.

The work we did not only reversed her cancer, but it also healed health issues that I was not aware that she had: chronic painful urination, a chronic scratchy sore throat, and a pattern of not speaking up for herself.

She shared with me that the positive tingling energy in her breast from the work stayed with her for a couple of days and she could no longer find the lump. It is well over a year later and her condition continues to be stable.

Use this knowledge now to effect your own complete healing. If you don't have a health issue use it to prevent ill health, disease, or to create your body's perfect health. Experiencing repeated emotions or patterns indicates negative energy buried within you that could turn to a physical health issue. Why not transform them now before they manifest physically.

Spiritual Drawing, Journaling, & Dreaming

Spiritual Drawing & Journaling

Throughout this book, there are samples from my journals. My journaling included advice that I received during meditation, automatic writing, documentation of my healing experiences, and drawings.

Writing and drawing are very therapeutic, but they are also an excellent manifestation tool. I teach my clients to draw what they want, or to write a story about it to bring the manifestation forward into the present. It is a great exercise. It helps to put a focus on what you want to have happen, which is a straightforward form of intention setting.

What was unexpected during my healing was the desire to creatively express the healing work I was experiencing. After many of my deep sessions, visuals would come right out of me and onto paper in brilliant colors. I call these my spiritual drawings.

I have had clients who also become inspired to draw or paint after a healing session. Like my experiences, their drawings would organically flow from them. When this occurs, the drawing comes from the inside of you, almost akin to automatic writing. Drawings such as these offer an opportunity to interpret what the image means, providing insights that help in the healing process.

Images have enormous power, and images freed from deep within ourselves can change us profoundly. When an image emerges from within, we glimpse and feel the energy of the universe, and our very soul. I would encourage anyone who is healing to make the experiences you have in meditation or in deep healing sessions tangible through drawing and writing. This helps integrate the work into the present moment.

During this period, my body and my entire being responded positively to support practices like meditation, Qigong, and yoga. After each practice, I would feel enhanced in some way; such as feeling uplifted, at peace, totally cleansed, or connected to the higher order. As a result, I was compelled to draw how it felt when I engaged in them.

These intimate aspects of my healing were the most personal part of my experience. I am grateful that I followed the urge to document my experiences, and I hope that sharing them will give you a different window to view how treasured and life changing a healing journey can be..

I recorded so many experiences during this period, it would be impossible to share them all. However, I am including a few spiritual drawings and deep healing experiences that I hope will convey the emotional and spiritual aspect of my experience.

On July 28, 2007, I experienced a session where the sticky, negative core of the tumor was released. I had lots of support from my angels and guides for this work. The below drawing was done immediately afterwards.

The sticky, gooey
CORE emotion Released
7/28/07

On Sunday Aug 12, 2007, about six weeks into my journey, I had a pivotal healing experience where I physically felt the energy within my tumor shift. Afterwards, the tumor felt dormant. It was very deep work. I was in the zone for almost two hours! This is what I drew immediately after the session.

"Transformed"
from the Inside
out
Tiger, Michael, Snake,
Germaine, Butterfly
Assist. 8/12

I took some time to meditate and journal on my patio one early morning in September. I was struggling with a distressing intestinal problem, and I did not know yet that I had parasites. This is what I recorded in my journal while experiencing healing work in a meditative state. The drawing below was done immediately afterwards.

The energy of this new day is refreshing, invigorating - offering you hope - hope of a bright future. Hope that there is more than an abyss - the deep pit of abyss. Crawl out of it. Crawl up and out of this pit now. We will help you.

It was a long journey up; I needed help along the way. Once over the edge and on the top I notice that I am physically covered with crud from the abyss. Two angels spray crystal water – they hose it over me and through me to rinse off the slim and crud. They tell me that this crystal water is purifying, energizing and is full of love, light and intelligence. It feels great. It is warm and feels comforting.

Then I am directed to lie in the sun to receive warmth and nourishment. As I am basking in the sun, the psychic surgeons put frankincense oil on my forehead, throat, and chest. They told all negativity to leave my body now. They commanded it with authority. I joined them with my own mind and thoughts. The deeply rooted ants and beetles from ancient times and ancient contracts started leaving my body through the very pores of my skin.

I feel my intestines rattle. The surgeons give me a potion to drink – liquid gold diluted with gold leaf tea. Once consumed the energies in my intestines form into a ball from every crack and crevice of the inside of my stomach. Then it easily gets passed out of my body as a big bubble. When it leaves, it floats far away. Then I see Arch Angel Michael grab it and bring it into the light.

I feel a pinch and pressure in my neck. The surgeons give me peppermint oil to inhale through my nose and a drop for my tongue – opening me up – loosening up the space. The pent up fears, despair, disappointment, abuse, and lack of love, zoom up from my heart and throat into the opened passageway and out of my crown. They emerge as heavy tears floating in the air. St. Germaine catches them in his violet flame and transforms them into universal joy for our planet.

Morning Patio Healing
9/18/07

I feel lighter and the soft sounds from the wind chimes on my patio remind me of where I am. I bow to the Universe with gratitude and declare I am free of all remaining demons! Amen. Namaste.

Expelling Old Chi
Alice
7/21

A practice that both calmed and energized me was Qigong, a method of focusing on particular energy centers in and around the body. It helped to clear old, unwanted energy (chi) from within me and bring in new chi. I found it very beneficial to do a simple 15-minute Qigong routine in the morning. It set the tone for my day. The drawing above shows how I felt during my Qigong routine.

Dreaming

From a psychology perspective each dream and everything in the dream is about you. It is a message about you, something that you already know deep inside, but not on a conscious level yet. Dream symbols can represent aspects of what you are feeling about your life. For example, if your dream is about riding in your car with someone else driving, it can mean that you feel like you do not have control of your life or that you have given control over to another person. Analyzing dreams can be helpful for understanding what is buried within, and it can be the basis of healing sessions or useful information as to what needs to be healed in the subconscious.

Another type of dream is a message dream. For example, I had dreams that indicated the deaths of my Dad as well as my Mom prior to their passings. In the dream about my Mom, I learned something that I was supposed to do. Initially it didn't carry much weight, but when my Mom was is the process of passing, I remembered it and used it. It was very helpful in easing my Mom's transition.

I've known people who have a disease that received warnings or alerts in their dreams, before they were ever ill. I've also known those that trusted the dream and investigated it, helping them to take action before a health issue got worse.

When healing, and at all times of your life, it is possible to receive helpful information in your dreams. Trust it. Use it.

Images from dreams may symbolize your health condition or how to heal it. Use a dream received image in your guided imagery work. Since it came from inside of you, it is probably the best image to use. For example, if you have cancer and you keep seeing a bag of coal in your dreams, make the guided imagery for your cancer that bag of coal. See the coal being taken out of the bag, or lift the bag up and throw it away.

There are also releasing dreams that can support your healing. Many years ago, I had a period where I dreamed of myself living in other eras, dressed in garments from those periods. Most were troubling or fearful. What I now know is that I was releasing some of my past life trauma through my dreams.

If you find yourself having unusual dreams while you are healing, be okay with it. It is part of the process. It might be useful to keep a dream journal next to your bed. Write down your dream as soon as you wake up, so you can easily remember them. Your dream experiences can help you to heal.

Healing with Sound & Color

In my practice of transformational healing, I use both sound and color to enhance the healing process. Sounds and colors are pure energy, made up of vibrational patterns and wavelengths. They work well with other energies, and I am honored to be able to work with them. Sound and color can be used to change energy patterns, density, or blockages that are inside of your body. We want to change those because they are related to ill health and disease. These pure energies are incredibly effective at supporting healing and maintaining health. Even animals respond well to the pure energies of sound and color.

It is interesting that each musical note corresponds to a color through its wavelength and frequency. There are seven major notes in a musical scale and seven colors in the rainbow. Variations appear as notes with sharps or combinations of notes, just as color variations occur when colors combine.

Healing with Sound

Sound healing brings the body back into a properly balanced, harmonious vibrational state. This leads to enhancing your health and calming your mental state.

Sound is one of the most ancient forms of healing, going back thousands of years. It has been an integral part of most ancient cultures healing practice. Sacred sounds can shift consciousness, raise your vibrational field, and bring you great peace and relaxation. There are many examples of ancient sound healing like the singing bowls from Tibet, whistling vessels from Peru, and toning and drumming from Native American cultures.

Sound Vibrations

I intuitively use my voice to tone. A tone is a sound that has no meaning and is pure. Sometimes my toning sounds like a singing bowl, a native chant, or a combination. I use this technique because:

- It runs energetic interference with your mind and thoughts, which helps you to stay in the deepest part of you, where your emotional memories are stored. I facilitate your healing so that you are able to have your own spiritual insights and growth. Healing works best when it is part of your mind, body connection. It can be difficult to find or stay in the deepest part of you because of endless mind chatter. Toning will help you find that special place and stay there, even if you have never attempted meditation before.
- Each tone corresponds with one of your chakras or energy centers. During toning, each chakra gets the benefit of vibrational sound healing. It is a wonderful way to keep your chakras clear and tuned.

- Toning can support the release of negative energy or keep you spiritually tuned in to receive an answer. It is common for a client to tell me during a session, "Keep toning, it is almost gone," or "Would you tone some more? I almost have the answer."
- The best part is that toning takes you to places and spaces inside of you, which you may not have experienced before. That is why toning is part of all of my CDs, guided meditations, and is an integral part of my healing practice.

For group work and meditations, I will use drumming and rattling, if appropriate. I especially like to use all three sound healing techniques, toning, rattling, and drumming, when conducting a group healing for our Earth. It seems fitting to use the customs of native people who lived in respect and harmony with our planet, when conducting a healing for the Earth.

Healing with Color

The full color spectrum that is found in a rainbow, are all parts of pure white light. After all, rainbows are created when white light is refracted and dispersed through raindrops, water vapor, or a prism. This light becomes the spectrum of seven colors; red, orange, yellow, green, blue, indigo, and violet. So, all colors are part of the whole, which can be used to support your health and well-being.

Each primary chakra is represented by a color of the rainbow. Healing and renewing your chakras always involves the use of color healing. For a more in depth look at chakras, see the 'Keep Your Chakras Clear & Healthy' section, page 15.

The warmer tones of color have a lower energy frequency, while the cooler colors have a higher energy frequency. Color aids in the cleansing and rebalancing of energy on the physical, mental, emotional, and spiritual levels.

While some people shine colored light directly on the body, I prefer to work with light energy while in a meditative, regressed state. I do this by asking the colored energy to enter the body or for one of my healing angels or guides to bring it in. From there, I use the colored energy to accomplish the purpose of the session. Most of the time my clients see the colors while in their regressed state, but everyone acknowledges their impact. I feel that working in this manner best supports the healing of the issue, while working at the cellular level. Even when working with color energies, intention setting is everything. When I ask the colored light to be there, I trust that it will be there doing its work, and it always does.

In my work, I have found that each color energy is best at performing certain tasks. I am happy to share a few examples with you, so you are able to bring these positive energies into your life, when you need them. Violet energy transmutes density, changing the state of affected cells from dark and dense, to light and bright. Green is a very healing, calming, and renewing energy. I like to use green after violet has done its work. I use bright yellow when happiness and joy are needed, or to offset prior energies like sadness or loneliness. I also work with colors that are not part of the rainbow spectrum. For instance, I use rosy pink to heal and cultivate the energy of self-love. I often use this rosy pink energy when healing the heart. Silvery blue light is great at protecting and stabilizing the work after completion. Gold is a powerful strengthening energy that is great at amplifying other healing energies.

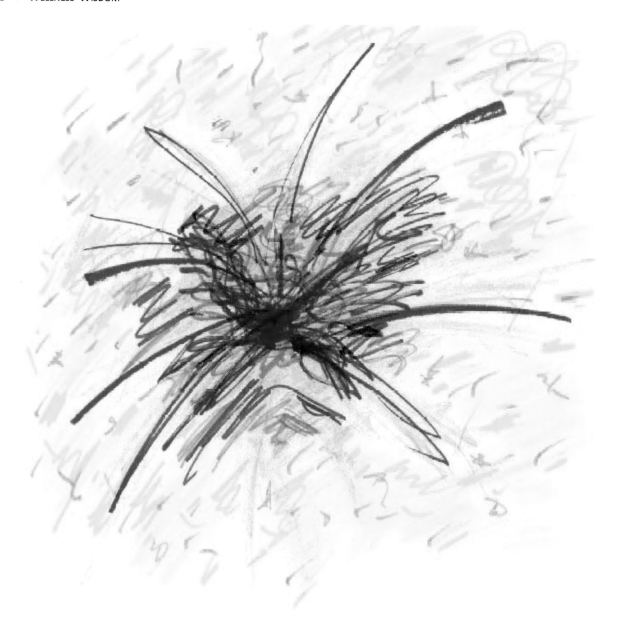

Healing from the Inside Out

This drawing best represents how I used color in my healing journey: The dense core issue usually showed itself as a dark orange, red, brown, and black combination. It is represented here as orange. I always work with violet, the energy of St. Germaine, to transmute dense energy. I usually use green, the energy of Archangel Raphael, for the healing and renewal of cells that had held the density, but I often use gold to accomplish the same result. Here, this is represented by green. I always use a gray-blue, the energy of Archangel Michael, to integrate, solidify, and protect the cellular changes. I often use yellow and pink to establish a new and healthier energy for the body and the entire being. Here, yellow and pink represent the joy and love that accompanies all transformational healing.

An Integrative Approach

In my healing practice, I use an integrative approach, incorporating many healing modalities. It is astounding how two different healing tools, like regression therapy and working with guides can come together in a wholly connected way during a session. This is best expressed by how complimentary sound and color energies are.

Color	Frequency / Wavelength		Chakra	Musical Note
Red	lowest	longest	Root	C
Orange			Sacral	D
Yellow			Solar Plexus	E
Green			Heart	F
Turquoise Blue			Throat	G
Indigo Blue			Third Eye	A
Violet	highest	shortest	Crown	B

When working on a health or emotional issue I work with sound and color healing in an integrative manner. I work with colored light energies, at the cellular level within the body, on the source of the issue that needs to be healed. This is usually buried in multiple places. I also bring color and sound energies to the chakra related to the emotional issue, as well as the chakras located physically near the health issue. This clears and tunes the affected chakras. I select different colors based on the focus of the work, meaning one color would be used for transmutation and another for healing. Throughout the session, I intuitively tone, which provides vibrational support for the healing process.

Give it a Try

Healing with sound and color has been around for thousands of years. They provided a vehicle for healing long before modern science and medicine. Why not try a healing experience with sound and color? They have no negative side effects and are free. For those who need more scientific logic, here is a thought: The mathematics of vibrational healing are explained and supported by the principles of Albert Einstein's work.

The Power of Crystals

When healing, I integrate many techniques beyond sound and color. Integrating the power of crystals is one that I want to make sure I share with you.

Crystals and gemstones have vibrational rates that correspond to their different properties. Each type of crystal has a unique set of properties that can be used to promote healing, resolve emotional issues, assist in manifesting your desires, open your spiritual connections, and absorb negative energy.

The easiest way to bring a crystal's beneficial vibration into your life, helping you attain good health and life goals, is to wear high quality crystal jewelry. If metal surrounds the crystal, it will inhibit the process, greatly reducing and possibly even eliminating the effects of the crystal. Alternatively, you can carry crystals in your pockets or in a small bag that you always keep with you. Like with other healing tools, using intention setting helps strengthen the process and the result. For example, "I intend that the amethyst crystal that I am wearing helps to transform all negativity in my life, including my own."

I seldom use crystals as a primary modality for healing, but I do use certain crystals to support my healing and spiritual work. I often place crystals near my clients, hold a crystal during the session, or give a crystal to a client for them to hold or place on their body. Throughout this book, I discuss how the placement of crystals in your home can enhance your environment. (See pages 96, 118, and 120.) Here are some of my favorite crystals:

- **Amethyst** is considered a master at healing. It provides protection, transmutes negative energy, and enhances spiritual abilities and awareness. It clears your energy, calms your mind, and enhances meditation. Amethyst helps to relieve emotional and physical pain, along with boosting many vital organs and systems in the body. It is beneficial for those that suffer with insomnia, digestion issues, or cellular disorders. When I conduct a healing session, on others or myself, I always have an amethyst nearby. This purple stone absorbs and transmutes negative energy that is transformed during healing and enhances spiritual connections needed for this work.

- **Crystal Quartz** is a powerful stone. It amplifies energy and regulates energy on physical and mental levels. It helps dissolve issues from past lives and enhances psychic awareness and abilities. Crystal quartz also stimulates the immune system. I have a crystal quartz stone that I like to hold when I'm doing inner work on myself or healing work on others. I feel it opens up and amplifies my spiritual communication and understanding.

- **Hematite** has outstanding grounding properties. It also protects, balances, and boosts one's self-esteem. Its grounding energy actually aids your ability to concentrate, focus, enhance memory, and remove mental limitations. Hematite supports healthy blood, alleviates cramps, and improves nervous disorders and spinal misalignment. Grounding yourself is always important while doing deep work, so I keep a hematite under my tailbone anytime I am doing energy work. If I feel the need for grounding support throughout the day, I will wear one close to my skin.

- **Rose Quartz** enhances healing through love, especially self-love. It releases blockages from unexpressed emotions, opens the heart chakra, heals a wounded heart, and teaches us how to love our self. This pink crystal aids the physical heart and circulatory system. It also attracts love to you. If I am working with a client who has a difficulty with self-love, emotional wounds, or problems with their heart or blood, I often give them a rose quartz to hold during the healing session. I placed this crystal on the center of my chest during my own healing sessions for breast cancer. Due to the proximity of my issue to my heart, and the emotional issues that were uncovered related to forms of love, rose quartz was one of the primary crystals I worked with to create my healing.

- **Selenite** is a powerful stone. It supports access to angelic consciousness, your ability to reach other lifetimes, and the enhancement of your insight and wisdom. For the physical body, it helps align the spinal column. If housed near other crystals, this stone keeps them clear and clean of negativity. I always use selenite when conducting past life work or aligning someone with their soul's purpose and future path, for both others and myself. For deep work, I will lightly run a selenite wand up and down the spinal column to open up the energy pathways, facilitating better energy flow during the work. I do this with each attendee of my day retreats, when the day is focused on deep inner work.

- **Charoite** is a stone of transformation. It aligns the heart and crown chakras, cleanses negative energies, and facilitates the acceptance of others. It is said to be the crystal of this decade, so wearing it helps you align with the universal energy of this present moment. I frequently wear this crystal around my neck, and I always wear it when I am conducting group energy work or retreats. It gives me the additional boost that I need to lead and work with groups versus one-on-one.

If you decide to wear crystals or place them in your home, it is important to cleanse them periodically either by burning white sage over them or washing them with salted water. After cleansing, placing them in the sun adds to the process. (It is important to note that not all crystals should be cleansed with water. Generally, soft crystals react poorly to salt and water, so they should be cleansed using other means. An example of a crystal that falls into this category is selenite.)

Incorporate Healing into Everyday Life

What happens when your healing is complete? Do you leave spiritual healing and energy healing behind? What if you are healthy and are not undertaking a healing, does healing still have a place in your life? Although most learn about healing techniques when they need them the most, like when embarking on a healing journey, their use is far reaching. I have found that it is useful to incorporate healing knowledge into everyday life to maintain ongoing health and well-being, on all levels. This not only keeps me physically healthy, but it helps me stay happy, grateful, and connected to all that is. Of course, it is easier to be in such a positive place after a deep healing at the cellular level has been accomplished.

Many of my clients share how they incorporate what they learn from working with me into their daily life. Some of their ideas are included here, along with my tips for everyday healing success. These techniques can easily become a natural part of your daily routine. Some of them require practice, but with each use, these techniques will require a little less effort.

Healing in the Present Moment

One of my clients had severe and chronic neck pains, which we healed together. She shared that because she now knows the cause of the pain she can use it to stay healthy and prevent the problem from reoccurring. She learned through a few sessions that she tends to bury thoughts or emotions about people who are a 'pain in the neck', in her neck. She was unconsciously holding onto the negative thought that someone or something was a pain, along with an associated negative emotion like anger, frustration, or irritation. Once she learned this, she now can conduct her own self-healing. When she notices something that feels like a neck pain starting to blossom, she immediately stops what she is doing, and asks herself, *"What did I just experience or think that feels like a pain in the neck?"* As soon as she acknowledges the cause in that moment, the neck pain disappears. Wow! This is certainly easier, healthier, and cheaper than taking a prescription medication, that has potential negative side effects. Furthermore, in her case, prescription medication had proved to be ineffective.

I believe in healing in the present moment, as soon as we are aware of something beginning. The cause is usually something we just recently experienced and/or thought. This makes it easy to identify and transform the trigger of your discomfort. Present moment healing not only is helpful at eliminating the potential health issue and associated discomfort, but it also plays another important role. When we eliminate the cause before it has an opportunity to go deeper inside of us, it becomes a powerful prevention tool in your arsenal against disease.

Working with Angels & Guides

Sometimes it takes more than acknowledging the negative thought and emotion we just held onto to be able to release it. This could occur for any number of reasons, but I want to share three of the most common: Your health issue like a cold or virus is entrenched in your body before you start to work on it. Your health issue is linked to a deeper pattern inside of you that you are unaware of. You just need some support, which is a good thing.

If I find myself in a similar situation, I ask for healing support to help ensure success. Let's say you start sneezing repeatedly for no apparent reason. Nothing you smelled irritated or tickled your nose, but you are still sneezing. If you can, close your eyes, center yourself, and ask for the violet light to come into your nose and help you to shift whatever is there. Ask yourself, "What am I holding onto in my nose?" Once again, since it just happened, it should be easy to acknowledge and clear. The violet energy is from the ascended master St. Germaine, a wonderful guide and healing partner of mine. Ask Germaine's energy to transmute this thought and emotion, as you say a positive affirmation like, "My nose is healthy," and your sneezing will stop immediately. When I am with other people, I do these steps quietly inside of myself without closing my eyes. They always ask, *"How did your constant sneezing suddenly stop?"*

Guides can also come in the form of animals, which is a common part of many Native American traditions. I find that asking for tiger, one of my animal guides, for courage when I feel I need it works well. I also like to call on snowy owl for wisdom and white horse to carry me where I need to go when I am uncertain or don't know how to proceed.

Working with angels is a wonderful support for all types of situations. If you are fearful or worried about something, ask Archangel Michael to hold onto it for you, or ask him to take it away. You can also ask him to cut the cords between you and your habit of worrying, for instance. Archangel Raphael offers great healing insight and wisdom. If you need help understanding the cause of your pattern or health issue is, or how to address it, he can guide you. Still yourself and ask for Raphael's healing wisdom to assist you.

Working with Colored Light Energy

In the earlier chapter on 'Healing with Sound & Color' I shared how to use colored light energies. For example, how violet energy transmutes the density of your buried negative emotions from your cells.

You can ask for specific colored light energies to be with you and they will be there. The best results are achieved when you are in a sacred meditation state, with clear intention. For instance, let's say that your intention is to shift the energy of sadness and transform it to happiness and contentment. While in meditation, ask what is causing the sadness. When you receive your answer, ask the violet energy to transmute it. Perhaps your body will let you know where you stored it by causing your heart to feel heavy or hot. Ask the violet energy to do its work in your heart. After you feel, see, or know the shift has occurred, ask the yellow energy of sunshine and happiness to fill your heart and being. Affirm this as your new way of being by saying, *"I am happy, joyful, and content."*

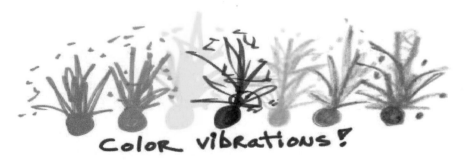

Color vibrations!

When doing a healing session on myself, I set the intention, and go into a deep meditation state. Often the work is done for me, as opposed to me guiding the work. Angels, guides, and colored light energy have all taken over some of my healing sessions. I witness the work and experience it happening in a deep state, but step back and allow the experience to unfold. After working with me, some of my clients have had similar experiences. The key is to be open to having this happen, and allowing it to occur when it does. Here is one client's description of allowing colors to heal her.

"After four years of cancer, I started working with Alice, who works with color. About a month into it, I really began opening up and believing in my ability to heal myself. I find now that whenever I feel tired or disconnected from myself, all I need to do is lie down, close my eyes, and let colors work with me.

"Not one of these meditations is quite the same as another, nor are the same colors or color combinations consistent. Sometimes a certain color will run its way through my body, dislodging any density. Sometimes they solidify and strengthen the parts of my body that feel weak. And at other times, colors have helped dissipate pain. I never directed them on what to do - it was more like me relaxing and letting them do their thing.

"As an example, I can remember once "working" on my bones. My entire skeleton became this intensely deep red - and as hot as fire - cleansing my bones of any waste or disease. When that was complete, they stayed that beautiful red but became covered in a very strong, stabilizing mahogany. And that is how I still picture them: the red burning up anything unwanted as the mahogany keeps them strong.

"My favorite time to work with colors is when I close my eyes and seem to become an astral body, nearly transparent, flying through a deep indigo universe, and eventually expanding into a thousand stars. It's delicious.

"I was introduced to the idea of healing with colors from my sessions with Alice. I am very drawn to color anyhow, so it's fitting that my spiritual guides would help my body to heal in this way. And it's a fantastic experience!" **S.P. Atlanta, GA**

Healing with Sound

What is rewarding about my healing sessions with clients is that most walk away with being able to use these techniques in their daily life. Most use my CDs with toning to help them keep their chakras healthy, maintain their energy, and support their meditations. In fact, people who have never worked with me but have purchased CDs, often write or call me just to tell me how profound their meditation experience is because of my toning. I even use my own CDs when I am feeling a little off, need an energy boost, or to maintain my chakras' health. It is so nice to turn on the CD player, stretch out, and allow the sounds to fill my core.

There are many ways to incorporate sound into your life. I find that having restful, harmonious sound in my home is very calming and healing. My preferences are the sounds of a water garden or wind chimes outside. I also favor CDs with nature sounds, beautiful chanting, or crystal bowls. When you go into meditation these types of sounds help to center you and move you to a deeper state. If you are seeking guidance, looking for healing support, or are just centering yourself, set your intention. Let the sounds carry you away to accomplish your goal.

My big tip here is not using music that has a familiar melody or that conjures up memories. This type of music will pull you back into your conscious mind, which is what you are trying to escape. That is why my preference is to use beautiful sounds that have no 'mental meaning'.

Be Aware of Your Thoughts & Moods

This may not seem like a big deal, but it is very important. Out of everything that I have shared, this is your proactive prevention path. When you are aware that you are thinking a negative thought or feeling a negative emotion, stop and shift it to the opposite. Sometimes this takes dedication and additional work. Why? Old habits, such as worrying or feeling lonely, can be hard to eliminate with one or two tries. However, each time it reappears it will be a little easier to shift. If you are fearful about your finances, for example, say to yourself, *"I am not going to fear, it is not healthy for me."* Release your fear to God. Then say, *"I am abundant. All my needs are always met. I am always taken care of. I do not need to know how. It is so."*

Incorporate Positive Affirmations into Your Life

One of my clients says that the affirmations that I give him are like a healing tonic. After every session, I email my clients the affirmations that we used during the session. These are directly opposite of the thought, emotion, or pattern that we shifted. I encourage my clients to read these everyday to support the new, healthy way of being. This particular client finds it helpful to record the affirmations, burn them onto a CD, and listen to them throughout his day. This is a great idea because your body takes commands from your mind, thoughts, and words. So hearing the affirmations in your voice is very potent. It also makes it easy for him, as he can just listen to them while doing other things or while in meditation.

I find it helpful after a successful healing to continue periodically saying my affirmations. I never stop using them, because it is an easy preventive measure and healing tool. When I take my morning walks with my dog, it will pop into my head to say; *"I am healthy dense bones. My bones support me easily and effortlessly. I am supported."* Early osteoporosis was something I successfully worked on several years ago, but I still affirm the outcome. I do not do this everyday, but about once every week or two. I also make sure that I lovingly hold and rub my breasts a few times a week and say, *"I love my breasts. They are healthy and whole in all ways. All cells and tissue in my breasts are healthy."* Even though those healing journeys are complete, the positive affirmations remind all parts of me that we are healthy in those, and all areas.

Conclusion: Spiritual, Mental, Emotional Aspect of Healing:

When incorporating healing techniques into your everyday life, they always work best <u>after</u> transformational healing at a cellular level has taken place. When the deep unconscious and subconscious cause of your issue has been removed, tools like healing in the present moment and sound energies work with little or no resistance. They may not be completely effective when the cellular work has not been done. All healing works best when you set intention and when you are in a quiet sacred meditative space within yourself.

The spiritual, mental, and emotional aspects of your body are critical to your complete healing. However, only 1/4 of this book is dedicated to it. Why? Once the root cause of your health issue and the associated density in your cells are transformed, it gives your body the ability to heal naturally. Why not do all that you can to support this healing in a rapid and complete manner?

What is interesting is that I was just starting to learn much of the health information in the remaining part of this book when my lump became dormant, about five weeks into my journey. It was a gift that I could not prove it. If I could have proved that there was nothing left to heal, I may not have learned what I am sharing next. The remainder of the book focuses on the ways to support your body's ability to heal naturally, and maintain health, even after your journey is complete. This has transformed how I live and eat on a daily basis.

You Are What You Eat!

My second priority on my healing journey was diet and nutrition. I want to share why I ate primarily alkaline foods, why I chose a macrobiotic diet, why eating organic foods is important for your health, the healing properties of some of my favorite foods, and much more. All of these are aspects that should be considered when choosing a diet and routine that is right for you, your health, and your lifestyle.

Unfortunately, most of us have been trained to eat for taste and for convenience. Stop and reflect on what your diet is doing for you. Eating for nutritional value seems to be long gone, even among members of the medical community. If you own a car and put gas in it, but forget to change the oil, it would start to break down. If you have the brakes checked regularly, but never rotated the tires, you would encounter other problems. It is the same with your body! What I eat, is driven by what I know will supply my body with the greatest health benefits and what will help me eliminate environmental toxins. How my food is prepared is driven by what helps it retain the most health benefits, while also supporting my body's ability to digest and absorb the nutrients easily.

I started using the following major criteria for selecting the foods that I eat. Not everything meets these criteria, but it helped me to make wise choices.

1. Is it in my recommended macrobiotic diet?
2. Is it alkaline?
3. Is it available organically where I live?
4. Are the health benefits or healing properties in line with healing and maintaining my health?

I avoided spicy and yeasty foods, even if they fell into the categories above, because cancer, bacteria, and fungus tend to breed in spicy and yeasty environments.

My Diet

I ate an organic, alkaline, macrobiotic diet that excluded all yeasty, spicy foods, alcohol, sugar, dairy, most meats, and coffee. It was high in fiber, with vegetables making up over 50%. I lightly cooked 95% of my food, without the use of a microwave. The exact foods that I selected within these criteria also have superior health and healing benefits that targeted my health issues and supported overall good health. I drank lots of pure water. I have slightly modified this approach now that I am in maintenance mode versus healing mode.

Alkaline Diet

From research within the first week of my healing journey, I learned that an alkaline diet is best for healing cancer and preventing disease in general. So I made sure that my foods were heavily alkaline. Luckily for me, I was already eating this way to a large extent. Over time, I tailored my diet considerably, not only from an alkaline perspective, but also from the basis of which foods supported the healing of my health issues, and what was good for my stomach's health.

Human blood pH should be slightly alkaline (7.35 - 7.45). Below or above this range could lead to ill health and disease. A pH of 7.0 is neutral, a pH below 7.0 is acidic, and a pH above 7.0 is alkaline. The main goal of an alkaline diet is to maintain a non-acidic pH.

How does an acidic pH occur in the first place? There are many contributors such as; emotional stress, toxic overload, immune reactions, or any process that deprives the cells of oxygen and nutrients. However, the biggest contributor is an acidic diet.

An acidic pH decreases the body's ability to absorb minerals and other nutrients, inhibits energy production in the cells, diminishes the ability to repair damaged cells, lessens the ability to detoxify heavy metals, makes us more susceptible to fatigue and illness, and creates an environment where tumor cells, cancer, parasites, fungus, and bacteria flourish.

Unfortunately, the typical American diet is very acidic. It contains too many acid producing animal products like meat, eggs, and dairy, along with too little alkaline producing foods like fresh vegetables. Additionally, we eat acid producing processed foods like white flour and sugar. We drink acid producing beverages like coffee and soft drinks. We use too many drugs, which are acid forming. Even artificial sweeteners are toxic and acid forming. One of the best things that you can do to correct an overly acidic body is simply change your diet.

A common rule of thumb to maintain health is that your diet should consist of 60% alkaline forming foods and 40% acid forming foods. To restore health, your diet should consist of 80% alkaline forming foods and 20% acid forming foods.

Let me emphasize that this does not mean you totally go alkaline. Your pH balance might shift too far the other way, and that is not healthy for you either. I include acidic foods that I know have other benefits like fermented products and white flaked fish.

The old rule 'all in moderation' applies. Eat acidic foods in moderation and alkaline regularly. With our lifestyle, you will probably eat acidic, unhealthy foods, unless you prepare and cook every meal, every day of your life, which isn't always possible.

Additionally, I have found that the division of acidic versus alkaline needs to be considered along with each food's health benefits and whether it is available organically. If fermented foods have great benefits but are acidic, let that be part of your 40%. If winter squash has multiple health benefits that target your needs but has a questionable alkaline pH and is not available organic, then maybe you only have it periodically. White flaked fish is not alkaline, but I added it for a good source of healthy protein. All of these can be part of your 40% acidic foods.

Some general direction: Stick to fresh vegetables, healthy nuts, and oils. Drink two or more liters of pure water daily. Make raw foods a small portion of your diet, but not aggressively. When I was healing, I lightly cooked everything, as it was easier for my stomach to digest and absorb the nutrients. My digestive system couldn't handle raw foods at that time, mostly due to parasites. Now I include raw foods in moderation.

Steer clear of fatty meats, dairy, cheese, sugar, chocolate, alcohol, and tobacco. Avoid packaged and microwave meals. Do not overcook your food, as it removes much of the nutritional value. Drink the juice from your lightly boiled or steamed vegetables - it contains the vitamins and minerals lost during cooking. Avoid spicy foods.

What combination of these principles you engage in is a personal judgment call, and I invite you to educate yourself. Start buying, cooking, and eating healthy foods and you will soon learn the right combination for your body. Set the intention that you will be guided to eat the foods that are best for you from the perspective of: alkaline, organic, macrobiotic, fermented, healing properties, good for the stomach, and good sources of fiber and protein.

Below is a summary list of some of the most alkaline and most acidic foods. If your food of choice is not on the list – please do your own research. This is not a complete list, but hopefully a springboard into the world of alkaline foods. In addition, some foods are neutral; they are neither alkaline nor acid. These are okay additions, but they will not help transform your intestinal environment from acidic to alkaline. I found from my research that there is disagreement in the categorization of some foods. One source might list brussels sprouts as acidic, and another has it as lightly alkaline – almost neutral. A source had apricots as acidic, but another point of view was that apricots are acidic before they fully mature, and are no longer acid after they mature. Many sources list tomatoes as acidic, but some feel there are new species that are alkaline.

Sample of Alkaline Foods

A rule of thumb is that a diet should consist of 60% alkaline forming foods and 40% acid forming foods to maintain health or 80% alkaline and 20% acidic to heal and transform health.

Fats & Oils

Avocado	Flax	Olive
Evening Primrose	Hemp	

Fruits

Apples	Pear	Some Varieties of Grapefruit
Avocado	Raisins	Some Varieties of Tomatoes
Lemon	Rhubarb	Watermelon
Lime		

Seeds, Nuts & Grains

Almonds	Pumpkin	Sprouted Seeds
Flax	Sesame	Sunflower

Vegetables

Artichokes	Chives	Lettuce
Asparagus	Cucumber	Onion
Beetroot	Garlic	Peas
Broccoli	Ginger	Radish
Cabbage	Grasses	Spinach
Carrot	Green Beans	Turnip
Cauliflower	Kale	Watercress
Celery	Leeks	

Sample of Acidic Foods

Convenience Foods

Chocolate	Microwave Meals	Tinned Foods
Fast Food	Powdered Soups	
Instant Meals	Sweets	

Drinks

Alcoholic Beverages	Dairy Smoothies	Soda
Black Tea	Fruit Juice	
Coffee	Milk	

Fats & Oils

Corn Oil	Margarine	Sunflower Oil
Hydrogenated Oils	Saturated Fats	Vegetable Oil

Fruits

Nearly all fruits that are not listed in the alkaline section are acidic.

Meats / Protein

Beef	Dairy Products	Milk
Cheese	Eggs	Pork
Chicken	Fish and Seafood	Turkey
Cream	Ice Cream	Yogurt
Crustaceans	Lamb	

Miscellaneous

Artificial Sweeteners	Soy Sauce	White Flour
Honey	Tamari	
Most Condiments	Vinegar	

Seeds & Nuts

Cashews	Peanuts

What was in My Acidic Percentage?

These are the acidic foods, along with foods that had questionable acid levels, which were included in my diet. All of them have health benefits and many are sources of protein.

Fish (frequently), Yogurt, Eggs (occasionally)
Blueberry (moderately), Apricot, Cherries (occasionally)
Sauerkraut and other Fermented Foods (moderately)
Legumes, Lentils, Brown Rice (frequently)
Brussels Sprouts (moderately)
Tamari (moderately), Honey, Vinegar (occasionally)
I also included supplements that I needed for my health that are acidic like Vitamin C, Magnesium, etc.

I was advised not to eat garlic and ginger raw, as they tend to be hot and spicy. I learned however, that cooking them reduces this effect. Because research suggests that cancer can breed in spicy environments, I didn't want to risk eating them raw, even though ginger and garlic are alkaline. During my healing journey, I only included them in my diet as cooked. Mushrooms are considered alkaline and wheat is only mildly acidic, but I avoided both as they are yeasty. Cancer, bacteria, and fungus also tends to breed in yeasty environments. Moreover, I added turmeric for its healing benefits, even though it is mildly spicy.

Since the time of my healing journey, I have added more raw garlic and ginger into my diet, because they have such good health benefits. I have also added back in an occasional cup of coffee or glass of wine, both of which are acidic and should be included in moderation.

Macrobiotic Diet

One of the first things I did after I learned of my diagnosis was to research alkaline foods. Since most vegetables are alkaline and there are many proponents of eating raw vegetables, especially for healing cancer, I began eating mostly raw foods. At first, the raw vegetables and special homemade raw blended drinks gave me a great energy boost. Wow! However, after a couple of weeks, my stomach was agitated and I longed for something warm. I was trying to heal my body, and my body wanted warm nourishing foods, not cold raw foods.

I was encouraged to look into a macrobiotic diet. I read about it and talked to several people who lived a macrobiotic lifestyle. I learned the basics of the macrobiotic approach.

This approach embraces the idea that the primary foods for humankind are whole grains. The second are vegetables, which should be locally grown and eaten in season. Animal products are not recommended, nor are processed foods. Grains, legumes, vegetables, seaweed, fermented soy products, and fruit are combined into meals according to the principle of balance known as yin and yang. What does that mean? Some foods are over stimulating, exhausting the body and mind. These are classified as extreme yin. Examples include sugar, chocolate, and dairy. Foods that are heavy or dense create stagnation if they are consumed in excess. These are considered yang. Examples include meat, eggs, and poultry. Foods like whole grains, vegetables, beans, sea vegetables, fruit, nuts, and seeds create a balance within our body. These balancing foods are the core of a macrobiotic diet.

It all made sense to me. The energy principles of this approach are complimentary to acupuncture, which I was using to support my body. However, I was overwhelmed with the amount of work it would take to be truly macrobiotic. I was told that you lightly cook most everything. Raw foods are excluded, except for select seeds and nuts. You never use the microwave, not even for warming something up. Fruit is poached or dried, and eaten separately from your meals. Foods are consumed in certain combinations. That is a lot of work for three meals a day with a lot of pans and dishes to wash. I was already struggling to have the time and energy to engage in my healing protocols while working and getting extra rest.

I decided to have a phone consultation with a macrobiotic counselor with the request that the recommendations be based on my diagnosis of breast cancer and my lifestyle. My major lifestyle concern was that I travel one to three hours to conduct events and I needed something that I could snack on in the car or eat for a quick lunch. I could not bring my kitchen with me. The counselor gave me diet guidance, which was a slightly modified macrobiotic approach.

What I learned from my consultation was that the human body has evolved (evolution of the species) over the ages to being accustomed to eating cooked foods. Think about it, only in the last 40-50 years have fresh fruits and vegetables been available year round. Prior to that time, you had to cook and can them in order to preserve them for the rest of the year, or only eat local fresh foods in their season. Our intestines have evolved to being used to primarily digesting cooked foods, not raw. When you eat a heavily raw diet it is harder to digest, and therefore, is often uncomfortable to your stomach.

Over cooking is also not advisable, as you lose the food's nutrients. The macrobiotic approach suggests lightly boiled or steamed vegetables with occasionally sautéing in olive oil. It proposes that only 0-5% of your entire diet be raw.

I also added what my Mom taught me. Save the juice from cooking your vegetables and drink it right away. This ensures that you get any nutrients that were lost in the cooking process. (Thanks, Mom!)

The Diet I Embarked on Included:

A few ideas for preparation and cooking are in the 'Recipe' section, page 89.

Grains:

Millet, Brown Rice, Quinoa, with some Barley. I was told to add a pinch of sea salt to the cooking water, and to combine two grains together. Today for convenience, I cook one grain at a time 70% of the time and cook two grains together the other 30% of the time.

Vegetables:

Best: Broccoli, Collards, Turnip, Turnip Greens, Carrot
Good: Acorn Squash, Arugula, Cauliflower, Kale, Mustard Greens, Scallion, Watercress, Leek, Onion

Dried shitake mushrooms were also on the "okay" list, but I chose not to include them. I did not want to put fungus into my stomach, and mushrooms are fungus.

Unfortunately, I could not digest greens because of my stomach (unknown parasites at that time), so I had to eliminate them. However, I would cook them and drink the juice. After I cleared the parasites and patiently worked to get my digestive enzymes and pH back in harmony, I was able to reincorporate beet greens, kale, collards, and other greens into my diet. These are a key part of my diet today.

For my lifestyle issue of eating while traveling, I was told that I could have an occasional carrot/celery raw drink. It was diluted with lots of water and sipped slowly throughout the day. It agreed with my system and filled me up.

Herbs:

Daily: Rosemary, Thyme
To Taste: Basil, Bay Leaf, Fennel, Sage

I tried to include rosemary and thyme everyday because of their healing properties. Other herbs were included as I cooked my food, primarily to add flavor. Since I lowered my salt intake and lessened my use of spicy condiments, I looked for new, healthy ways to make savory dishes.

Beans & Lentils:

Best: Chickpeas, Hummus, Lentils, Navy, Fermented Soy Products like Tempeh and Miso
Good: Great Northern, Anasazi, Aduki

It was suggested that I eat these 12-16 times a week. I did not eat them at that level, but I did include them in my diet on a very regular basis. Because I chose to have a higher percentage of my diet be vegetables, it was impossible for me to follow this recommendation.

For my lifestyle, when I didn't have time to cook, I was told that a good alternative is *Amy's* brand of organic lentil and black bean soups.

Seeds & Nuts:
Almonds and Pumpkin seeds only. No nut or seed butters.

I added brazil nuts sparingly for variety, since they are good for healing cancer and are a complete protein. Recently, I added back in sesame seeds for their health benefits.

Oils:
Sesame and Olive only

Seafood:
Salmon and Fresh White Flaked Fish like Sole, Flounder, and Haddock. I added local caught Grouper and Snapper as an extension of White Flaked Fish.

Fruits:
Best: Apple, Blueberry, Lemon, Lime
Good: Pear, Apricot (dried), Raisin, Cherry (dried)

For my lifestyle, it was acceptable for me to have an occasional raw apple (versus poached), and I was told I could eat them with raw almonds for a snack. Usually fruit is only eaten alone. Blueberries could be eaten raw or dried. With research, I learned that dried blueberries are good for remedying diarrhea, so I was primarily eating them dried.

Seasonings & Condiments:
Frequent Use: Umeboshi Plum Paste, Tamari Soy Sauce
Occasional Use: Ginger Root, Garlic

Seaweeds:
Best: Nori, Wakame, Kombu, Arame

I averaged about 1/4 sheet of nori a day, four days a week. I added a few pieces of wakame to my soups, rice, and vegetables about five times a week. These gifts from the sea are jammed packed with health benefits. Today I use both, but less frequently.

Recommended Proportions for the Average Macrobiotic Diet:
30-40% Whole Grains
40-50% Beans, Lentils, Seeds, Nuts, Oils
20% Vegetables

I changed the proportions for my diet to being much higher in vegetables, as I was trying to heal cancer. My proportion of vegetables was over 50%.

The macrobiotic counselor gave me no direction on organic versus non-organic. I made the choice to follow the recommended diet, while focusing on including as many organic foods as possible. Sometimes I would eliminate a food since I could not find it organically grown. Other times I would include specific non-organic foods, since the healing benefits were important for my health issues.

After about six weeks, I was very tired of fish as my major protein. That is when I seriously started incorporating miso and tempeh as protein sources. I added organic eggs a few times a week. I included avocados periodically, and was happy to learn that they contain a small amount of protein. For an easy snack food, I made my own guacamole without spices and tomatoes. I also added a slice of whole grain bread, which contained little or no wheat, up to once a day to spread humus on.

Well into 2008, I discovered that I could buy brown rice pasta. Yeah! I can have healthy pasta with garlic and olive oil. I also found brown rice crackers and organic crackers that I eat with hummus and guacamole. Another nice snack is poached apples or pears dusted with cinnamon and allspice. It tastes like a dessert.

Beverages:
No Coffee, Liquor, Soda, Wine, etc: I have since modified this to include one to two cups of coffee a month and an occasional glass of wine.
Lots of Pure Water and Herbal Teas: I chose herbal teas with the best benefits for my health issues.

After a lot of research, I decided on spring water instead of purified or filtered. I also found a pitcher called *Santé Energizer.* It charges your water to a higher vibration. This means that you are always drinking water that adds a healthy vibration to your body. This has a positive impact on healing and maintaining health. I let my spring water sit in the pitcher for 12 hours or more, which is the suggested time it takes for the water to fully charge. This was the only water I drank, except when I went out to dinner, which was infrequent during this period. In general, it is important to put the purest water, without chemicals or other toxins, into your body. Today I still use the Santé pitcher to maintain my health, and I drink a combination of filtered and spring water.

Since the time of my initial consultation, I learned that macrobiotic is a cleansing diet – making it a good choice when you are detoxifying your body, or trying to heal a health issue. Maybe that is why those that stick with a macrobiotic diet are thin.

Two years after the beginning of my journey, my diet is about 80% macrobiotic. I have added back about six homemade raw green vegetable drinks a week, and occasionally cooked vegetables that were not on my diet like asparagus, green beans, bok choy, radish, and artichoke. I have added other fermented foods like sauerkraut and komboucha, which I discovered by inquiring about fermented foods at my local health food store. I eat a fresh salad about five times a week now – my preferred salad greens are romaine and arugula. Seaweed is still included regularly, but less frequently compared to when I was on my healing journey. However, other than these minor tweaks, I am still on board with my original healing diet. This is how I live now and it has become natural for me. In the beginning, each choice took time and consideration, but as I have grown accustomed to this diet, it has become an easy part of my life and daily routine.

When I eat at a friend's house or at a restaurant, I make the best choices from what is offered and I bless the food as healing. When pizza is the only choice, I will eat and enjoy it. Every once in awhile I eat a slice of crusty bread with oil or will snag a few potato chips. However, I have to admit that I do not do this often, because I just feel better when I eat healthy.

One final tip: When I was on my healing journey, I tried to make sure I included all my supplements, foods, and protocols everyday. This became stressful. Everything fell into place for me when I started to relax and approach everything organically. If I missed the evening's dosage of lymph herbal pills, or forgot to use nori that day, I didn't worry about it or try to add it in at 11:00pm that night. I just did the best I could each day.

Currently, I have lots of healthy foods and supplements in my pantry and refrigerator. Each day I consume what feels right at the time. However, I always make sure I eat my vegetables every day, especially greens and broccoli.

You may be thinking, "What does she eat?" The following sections are dedicated to the foods that I ate with explanations on why those foods were good for me. Then please look at the 'Healing Foods' section (page 53) for their health benefits and the 'Recipe' section (page 89) for ideas on how to prepare them.

Sources of Protein

I have already discussed some of the health risks with many of the traditional sources of protein:

Seafood: Shellfish, fish steaks, non-white flake fish can hold microorganisms, bacteria, and mercury.
Beef, Pork, Lamb, and Chicken: Lots of animal fat, cholesterol, unhealthy hormones, and antibiotics.
Milk and Milk Products: Hormones and antibiotics, possible negative impact on phlegm and lymph.

Here are some healthy protein sources that I use. If you can't find something at your grocery store or health food store, ask if they can order it for you. You can also purchase some of these items on the internet.

- White Flake Fish (Wild Flounder, Grouper, etc) and Wild Salmon
- Organic Eggs (hormone and antibiotic free) - it is good to cook it so the yoke is soft, as it has many health benefits that way (i.e. over light or poached)
- Tempeh - fermented soy product with a nutty taste
- Beans and Legumes, especially when combined with rice or grains
- Hummus – a delicious bean dip
- Avocados - offer some protein
- Nuts and Seeds
- Grains - especially quinoa
- Miso Soup
- Tamari Soy Sauce – a fermented seasoning
- Brussels Sprouts – when combined with rice or grains they provide a complete protein
- Royal Jelly – a supplement

Sources of Fiber

A Fiber Rich Diet is Important! Why? It...
- Helps maintain normal cholesterol levels and prevent heart disease.
- Helps maintain normal blood sugar levels.
- Helps keep unwanted pounds off.
- Supports bowel regularity.
- Prevents and heals both constipation and diarrhea.
- Supports the healing of irritable bowel syndrome.
- Supports a healthy environment for your stomach.

Sources of Dietary Fiber Consistent with the Diet that I Have Been Discussing:
Excellent sources include: Greens, Cauliflower, Broccoli, and Swiss Chard
Very good sources include: Romaine Lettuce, Celery, Spinach, Flax Seeds, and Artichoke
Good sources include: Apricots, Sweet Potato, Beets, Cruciferous Vegetables like Broccoli and Cabbage, Winter Squash, Carrots, Lentils, Beans, Hummus, Onions, Blueberries, and Grains like Quinoa, Millet, Brown Rice, and Barley

In general, most vegetables and fruits have some fiber. The ones listed here are healthy fiber dense foods. It is interesting to note that the majority of the foods recommended in this book offer some fiber.

Surprisingly, many of the herbs that I listed in the 'Healing Foods' section are also great sources of fiber by their weight. For example, a tablespoon of rosemary has nearly 1.5 grams of dietary fiber. Oregano, cinnamon, and thyme are also fiber dense herbs.

The Importance of Water

Water is essential. Without enough fluid intake, dehydration can set in quickly. Severe dehydration can lead to death within a few days, whereas you can survive for weeks without food. It is important that your beverage of choice be pure water, not soda or sweet tea.

Approximately 55-60% of our body weight is water. Your body depends on water to keep your cells and bodily systems running smoothly. Water is critical for regulating body temperature, along with delivering oxygen and nutrients to your entire body. Water supports bodily functions at the cellular level and is crucial for the removal of waste products through the formation of urine.

Don't let thirst be your only trigger for drinking a glass of water. As we age, we gradually lose our thirst sensation. Develop a routine of intentionally monitoring your water intake, so you know that you are getting your daily requirement. Many recommend multiplying .5 oz of water by your body weight, and then dividing by eight to get the number of 8 oz cups you should drink in a day. Example: 150 lbs x .5 = 75 oz or 9.3 cups of water daily.

What about water temperature? Most research points to room temperature water being better for you, especially after a meal. Cold water solidifies any oil that has just been consumed, slowing its proper digestion. Overall, warm or room temperature drinks, are preferred to cold drinks as a simple tool for better digestion.

Other Considerations

Cooked versus Raw

In the macrobiotic section, I discussed how a heavily raw diet could be harder to digest, even agitating to your stomach. I chose a macrobiotic diet for many reasons, including its ability to nourish my intestines that were under attack by parasites, and to heal my body and spirit.

My body was craving warm nourishing foods, not cold raw foods. Most times our bodies truly know what is best for us, and cravings are a clue into our body's needs. So, when raw food wasn't agreeing with me, and my body was craving warm foods – I listened.

However, I did include a few raw foods:
- Nuts and seeds, primarily almonds and pumpkin seeds
- Blueberries, avocado, sauerkraut, and kombucha
- Dried apricots, blueberries, cherries, and goji berries
- An occasional apple or pear
- A very occasional salad
- Seaweed

When I completed my healing and gave my digestive track a chance to rebound, I started to re-introduce raw foods gradually into my diet. Why? I missed the energy boost from my blended green smoothies and raw salads.

Why Raw?
A raw food diet generally consists of unprocessed, uncooked plant foods, such as fresh vegetables, fruits, sprouts, seeds, nuts, grains, beans, legumes, dried fruit, and seaweed. Plant-based foods, in their uncooked state, are considered raw and alive. These live foods contain a wide range of vital life force nutrients and enzymes.

Heating food above 116 degrees Fahrenheit is believed to destroy enzymes, along with diminishing the nutritional value and life force of food.

Proponents of the raw food diet believe it has numerous health benefits, including increased energy, weight loss, and improved skin appearance.

Why Cooked?
Critics of the raw food diet do agree that some enzymes become inactivated when food is heated. Their point of view is that it doesn't matter because the body uses its own enzymes for the digestion process. In addition, cooking makes certain phytochemicals more easily absorbed by the body, such as the beta-carotene found in carrots. A phytochemical is a chemical substance found in plants, including fruits and vegetables, that's biologically active but not nutritive. Phytochemicals exhibit a potential for reducing the risk of cancer along with many other diseases.

My experience is that if you lightly cook or steam your foods, and then drink the cooking water that is left in the pan, you obtain most of the food's nutrients.

The human body has actually changed in response to eating primarily cooked foods. Some of these changes are that our jaws and teeth have become smaller, our stomachs have shrunk, and our small intestines have grown longer, lengthening the digestive surface area.

Other theories indicate that a raw-only diet may not be appropriate for people with certain constitutional types or people living in colder climates.

Is There a Balance?
Unlike viewpoints that are all or nothing, I feel that a combination diet is great. A diet that is 100% raw is probably extreme for most of us. Sometimes we focus too much on the differences instead of the similarities.

So where does that leave me now, after I have healed myself of serious health issues?

- I continue with my modified macrobiotic diet – it determines most of my food choices.
- I have reintroduced blended greens and vegetable drinks into my routine gradually, instead of everything being lightly cooked. Today, I try to have one each day, preferably in the morning or early afternoon. I average about five a week.
- I eat a raw salad (mostly greens with some vegetables) about six times a week.
- I added young sprouted raw legumes to my diet in moderation. I put them in my salads and raw drinks.
- All the other raw foods that I incorporated into my healing diet remain the same: raw nuts, seeds, apples, pears, blueberries, avocado, sauerkraut, komboucha, and dried fruit especially apricots and cherries.

Today I like my combination diet of raw and lightly cooked foods. It works for me! What is interesting is that I get the best of both worlds. The recommended foods in raw and macrobiotic diets are very similar. Yeasty foods, sugary foods, and most animal products are generally excluded from both macrobiotic and raw diets. I include foods that have great health benefits, but now some are eaten raw and most are lightly cooked.

An all raw diet agitates my body. I have found that my body responds to warm grains and vegetables, but it also enjoys the energy boost from raw drinks, salads, and fruits in moderation. Listening to your body and doing what feels right is very important.

Important Eating Tips

Eating raw and cooked foods at the same time can impede digestion of their nutrients. For optimum digestion of your food's health value, it is best to eat them separately.

Fruits should be eaten separately whether they are raw or cooked. When fruit is raw, it is even more important to eat it on an empty stomach. Why? The benefits of fruit, like its detoxification properties and its ability to supply you with good energy, are more readily absorbed when it is the only thing your stomach is digesting. This process is hindered when combined with other foods.

The fruit nutrients, when eaten separately, go straight through the stomach into the intestines. The intestines are where your food's nutrients are absorbed. When eaten with another food, the health benefits are blocked from being properly absorbed. Anytime fruit encounters other foods in the stomach, bloating and gas are more likely to occur.

I chose to eat fruit, whether it is raw, lightly poached, or dried, as healthy snacks in-between meals. This helps me properly absorb all of the fruit's nutrients and avoid any negative effects like bloating.

More to Think About

Because I primarily eat raw at home, I have control over the preparation. Why is this important? Microorganisms, bacteria, and parasites are more common in uncooked foods. When your food is properly cooked, it kills these unwanted elements. Remember, when you travel to underdeveloped countries you are told never to eat raw foods or drink water that is not bottled. There is a reason for that and it can happen in this country too. So, I suggest eating raw at home and eating mostly cooked when you are out.

Everyone has to listen to his or her own body. I suggest that after experiencing a diet of healthy, organic, lightly cooked foods with a macrobiotic approach, notice how your body reacts as you reincorporate raw foods. If it handles it, then you most likely can continue to include raw foods. If your stomach cramps or is gassy for long periods (some initial discomfort should be expected), you should think twice about having too many raw foods in your diet.

Organic versus Non-Organic

It became obvious to me as I continued my journey that I was going to have to do a lot of detoxing. The goal was to clear my body of the buried toxins from the environment, and from the foods and beverages that I consumed over the years. Why would I knowingly put in more toxins by eating non-organic foods? It didn't make sense. Putting toxins and hormones into your body by eating foods that are not organic gives it something else to fight off. Does it make sense to leave less energy for the main healing event? For those that are not trying to cleanse or heal, non-organic foods, over time, could cause your body to become dysfunctional.

Food with insecticides, hormones, and environmental funk are just not good for your body. Chicken, cattle, eggs, milk, cheese, and yogurt that are not organic probably have unnatural hormones added through their feed. The purpose of the hormones is to make the livestock grow quickly, maximizing profits. Once educated, why would one want to eat these foods? They are not healthy for you.

A client shared that he attended a kinesiology demonstration at a national convention. Kinesiology is a form of body testing. The demonstration was testing what foods the body liked or didn't like. The volunteer was lying down, and a bag of cabbage was placed on his stomach. It tested positive – the body liked it. Then another bag of cabbage was placed on the subject's stomach. It tested really negative – the body did not like it at all. The audience asked, "What is the difference? It is the same vegetable!" The demonstrator explained that the first cabbage was organic while the second one was not. Clearly, the body did not like the vegetable with toxins and insecticides. Nor does yours.

I learned that white flaked fish and salmon are the only types of seafood I should eat. All fish steaks, as well as shellfish, can hold onto bacteria, microorganisms, or mercury. We need to buy and order <u>wild caught</u>, not farm fed fish. We do not know what is in the feed of the farm fed salmon, tilapia, and other fish. I know that they are cheaper to buy, but your body's health is worth it. When I eat out, I always order wild caught salmon or white flake fish when it is available. It is also what I buy and cook at home.

I experienced the hard way that eating chicken, brown rice, and vegetables may seem healthy, but when I woke up at 3:00am with my stomach flopping, I knew that I could no longer handle the hormones in the chicken. Now if the only choice is chicken or steak I will eat a few bites of it, and fill up on whatever vegetables are being served.

Many experts feel that hormones in animal products, even those that are added through feed, are causing younger girls to menstruate sooner than in previous generations. There are also more women in their 20's and early 30's that are being diagnosed with breast cancer. Many feel that the hormones in livestock feed are accelerating what would normally take years to develop, or possibly would not develop at all.

In many communities, organic foods are becoming more readily available. My local health food store was a great resource for many organic foods. If you live in an area where this is not so, I encourage you to drive the extra distance and pay the extra money to buy and eat organic foods, wild caught fish, and organic eggs. You are worth it!

Diary, Wheat, Yeast, & Sugar

You can now find organic dairy products such as milk, cheese, and yogurt in nearly every grocery store. I chose not to eat organic cheese, as it is yeasty. Yeasty foods are not good for the stomach, as they tend to foster the growth of bacteria, fungus, and disease, such as cancer. They also can make your stomach feel puffy and swollen. I had already cut out yeasty foods from my diet prior to this journey. I had a slightly round stomach, and my energy level felt low. When I cut out yeasty foods, my stomach became flat, my energy levels went up, and I felt better overall.

Yeasty foods include cheese, wheat, wheat gluten, peanuts, and mushrooms, which are an actual fungus. I maintained the exclusion of yeasty foods on my healing journey and beyond - no wheat, and no cheese.

Sugar breeds yeast problems like Candida albicans. Candida normally lives in your body - especially in the gastrointestinal tract and genital tract. When your immune system is strong, Candida yeasts cause no problems. However, a sugary, yeasty, acidic diet can foster its growth. Also, when you take broad-spectrum antibiotics, they knock out friendly bacteria, giving the Candida an opportunity to multiply. There are many who feel that there is a direct connection between fungus, such as Candida, in your body and cancer. I always take a strong probiotic everyday to help support the health of my stomach. My supplement consists of approximately 15 strains of stomach friendly bacteria and 35 billion microorganisms per serving.

I choose not to drink organic milk, as it causes existing phlegm and mucus to get thicker, which is unhealthy. For those who are allergic to milk products, and many are unaware that they are allergic, they can have a reaction where the body actually produces more phlegm and mucus, not just making it thicker.

There also seems to be a connection with excess phlegm and mucus, and an unhealthy lymphatic system. When healing any disease, especially breast cancer that is linked to the underarm lymph glands, why ingest anything that could impact the lymphatic system's ability to flow freely? Having healthy, free flowing lymph is critical to maintaining health and preventing disease. Your lymphatic system is a key part of your immune system.

I have made one exception with dairy foods, two tablespoons of plain organic yogurt, about three days a week with cereal grains at breakfast. Why? It has the benefits of probiotics and fermented foods, which other dairy products, like milk, don't have.

As with anything discussed in this book, including having dairy in your diet, it is a personal choice. I suggest that you do your own research and if you do include dairy products, please choose organic.

Microwave: Yes or No?

Why should you consider limiting your use of the microwave? Much documentation indicates that the microwave might actually break down the healthy properties and nutrients in your food. If you take the time to purchase, prepare, and cook expensive organic foods, why risk that a microwave could deplete the food's goodness?

During my healing journey, I cooked and heated all my foods on the stovetop. I still do not use a microwave.

Your microwave oven sends microwaves into your home environment. The directions for the Santé Energized pitcher suggest that you do not place the pitcher near a microwave, because it could counteract the positive charge. A convection oven is a good cooking alternative. A counter top convection oven or toaster oven are less expensive options.

There are proponents of the microwave that say that there are no known negative side effects. Since it is uncertain, I choose to play on the safe side and do not use it.

Note: For more information on microwaves, see 'Maintain a Healthy Home & Site Environment', page 118.

GM Food - Genetically Modified Food

A GM food means that genes from animals or from other plants are genetically manipulated into the cells of food plants to create super crops. This is the same idea as hormones being added to livestock and farm fed fish. These crops are larger, more resistant to bugs, and have a longer shelf life. An example: the genes of a fruit fly are injected into a tomato attempting to make the tomatoes repel the flies. Guess what? You are now eating the genes of a fruit fly without knowing it.

This is upsetting. Some estimates state that 60-70% of processed foods contain genetically modified ingredients. Crops such as soybeans, maize, cotton, and rapeseed oil are some of the most commonly modified. This means that many cereals, snack foods, and foods made with cottonseed and canola oils could be from genetically modified crops. It is frequently included in animal feeds as well.

The more that I live on this earth the more of a purist I have become. It takes more money to buy natural organic food and time to cook it properly – but my body is worth it, isn't yours?

MSG is Everywhere!

There is evidence that shows that MSG could triple the amount of insulin the pancreas creates, causing rats, and perhaps humans, to become obese. Links have been established between MSG and headaches, diabetes, dizziness, chest pains, stomach aches, asthma, depression, fatigue, bloating, and skin rashes.

If you look at labels, MSG is shockingly everywhere, even among many brand name foods. Monosodium glutamate, is also known as sodium glutamate or MSG. It is a combination of water, sodium and glutamate. Glutamate is an amino acid, one of the building blocks of protein and naturally occurs in a variety of foods. Today, MSG is mass produced and the concern lies in both the possible contaminates and that our body is unable to process the excess glutamate that we are consuming.

I recently learned that MSG is listed as an ingredient by other names, like 'hydrolyzed vegetable protein', and 'natural meat tenderizer' for example.

Research indicates that many of the popular chain restaurants include MSG in their menu offerings. Some people have started asking to see the list of ingredients at restaurants, believing that some dishes include MSG. Surprisingly, many do.

Why is MSG in so Many of the Foods We Eat?
Some researchers suggest that MSG is added to food for the addictive effect that it has on the human body. It can actually make people eat more. MSG is being added in larger and larger doses to pre-packaged meals, soups, snacks, and fast foods.

Do a little research on what foods contain MSG and you will find a long list of foods that most people eat regularly. One food that surprised me was anything that had parmesan cheese might contain MSG. That includes a salad that people like to think of as healthy – caesar salad.

I am not an expert on this, but I am sure happy that my packaged and pre-prepared foods are pretty much limited to organic cereals that are without additives. Start reading your labels, and ask for the ingredient list at your favorite restaurants.

Healing Foods, Supplements, & More!

Healing Foods

The information in this section is good for preventing disease, maintaining health, and healing.

Thirty years ago, it was unheard of to suggest that cancer could be shut down by diet. Even today, diet advice is seldom part of a doctor's prescription for getting well, regardless of the type of health issue.

Interestingly, when I consulted with homeopathic doctors, nutritional counselors, herbal specialists, and other practitioners, they would recommend supplements, herbs, and the macrobiotic diet, but there was no mention of what foods could actually help heal my diagnosis of cancer.

Because I always had an interest in this area, I knew that foods have healing properties. I did my own research through books, the internet, and any other source I could find.

Food molecules are serious players in the life and death of our cells. Cells are the building blocks of our bodies, and everything around us. Specific components of certain foods perform tasks that help ensure our overall cellular health. When our cells are healthier, we are healthier. Studies have shown that some food cells have the ability to perform anticancer activities. They can interfere with the start of the cancer process within the nucleus of cancer cells. Preventing the core of the cancer cell from properly developing means that there is less of an opportunity for it to become a part of your body. Other food cells help to capture and dispose of free radical molecules that can lead to cellular damage and cancer. Some are even able to stimulate enzymes to eliminate carcinogens from the body and prevent carcinogens from being activated. A carcinogen is a substance or radiation that initiates or promotes the development of cancer within your body. Common examples of carcinogens are tobacco smoke, asphalt fumes, and exposure to gasoline.

Food can help fight cancer at every stage, from the first inception in a single cell to the tumor that was formed many years later. Food can also prevent and protect certain organs from a cancerous assault.

Yet when I talk to people who have tumors, or other forms of cancer, they are hesitant to change their diet. Incorporating these healing foods, especially when most of them are vegetables, can be hard to stick to when someone is accustomed to a meat, potato, and dessert way of eating. Another obstacle is that most of the healing foods require cooking meals at home, so convenience foods, fast food, and even foods that we once thought were healthy should no longer be a part of your diet. In my research, I found that most of what we as a society eat everyday is not healthy, and it is even true for those that try to be informed.

Building a strong biological barrier against cancer in your body offers hope of leading a cancer free life. Healing foods offer protection against the pollution and chemicals in the air, land, food, water, and in our bodies. Since we are bombarded with carcinogens, why not pump ourselves up with anti-carcinogens?

Look at it like ensuring that your body has a national guard to corral and push hazardous chemicals out of your body before they can settle in and do damage. Why not use the substances found in foods to block the effects of carcinogens before they can do damage?

Cruciferous Vegetables: Cabbage, Broccoli, & More!

Studies since the 1960's have shown that components of broccoli and cabbage can reach into living cells and stop cancer. Why is this not one of the main messages of cancer prevention and recovery from the medical community?

The research has been expanded to include all of the cruciferous vegetables like brussels sprouts, cabbage, cauliflower, broccoli, kale, collard greens, and turnips. Studies have shown that when people ate these vegetables often, they lowered their risk of cancer. In fact, the more they were consumed, the greater the therapeutic effect. Cruciferous vegetables contain antioxidants, along with being high in fiber, vitamins, and minerals.

If you start eating a lot of these veggies, please eat organic. We do not want to put environmental toxins into our bodies while trying to get the benefits of these healing and preventative foods.

Cruciferous vegetables are also good for intestinal health, helping to get rid of the yeasty foods that cling and thrive in little corners of your colon.

Broccoli seems to be the shining star of the group as it contains both carotenoids and cancer antidotes. Due to its abundance of chlorophyll, broccoli is strong at blocking cell mutations that often foreshadow cancer.

I try to eat lightly cooked broccoli every day. It has become my vegetable of choice because of all of the great research behind it as a healing and preventative food.

Greens, carrots, and cabbage are also big parts of my diet. Winter squash is a favorite of mine for both the taste and health benefits. It is not always available organically in my area, but because of its health benefits I include winter squash in moderation, once every couple months. Organic brussels sprouts are only available seasonally. Although I love to eat them, I choose not to eat non-organic brussels sprouts, as I do the winter squash. The reason is that other cruciferous vegetables, which I can easily find organically, have similar health benefits. Instead, I eat organic brussels sprouts with a passion when they are available seasonally.

Try the Health Benefit of Combining Dark Green & Orange Vegetables.
(Example: carrots with spinach, or kale with winter squash)

Many studies link the combination of dark green vegetables and orange vegetables as a powerful tool in fighting and protecting against cancer. Together they provide both beta-carotene and antioxidant carotenoids.

I decided to use this information to my advantage. During my healing journey and continuing today, I eat dark green vegetables like kale, collards, swiss chard, spinach, broccoli, and beet greens twice a day, every day. I add winter squash or carrots to the dark green vegetables about five times a week. This way, I am maximizing the health benefits from these healing foods.

Health Benefits by Food

This is a list of the healing properties for some of my favorite foods. Stock up and draw from the best pharmacy - that of your refrigerator and pantry. I have included the foods that I ate at all stages of my healing journey and even a few recent discoveries.

<u>Eat Your Veggies!</u>

At least 40% of your diet should be vegetables and that means more than salads. If you are healing, the percentage of vegetables should be higher. Most vegetables are good sources of fiber, vitamins, minerals, and much more.

Artichoke:
- A top ranking antioxidant super food
- Lowers cholesterol
- Supports liver and gallbladder health
- Low in calories and fat free
- High in fiber, magnesium, potassium, calcium, iron, and phosphorus
- Improves the appetite and digestion
- A natural diuretic - stimulates bile and urine
- Enhances the health and appearance of skin

Arugula:
- Rich in nutrients such as vitamins A and C, calcium, iron, beta-carotene, magnesium, and folic acid
- **Rich in phytonutrients, reducing the risk of cancer**
- Provides antioxidant activity
- Stimulates natural detoxifying enzymes in the body

Beets: Beet greens are less bitter than most greens and are a nice alternative to traditional greens.
- **Inhibits the development of cancer** – especially colon cancer
- Protects against heart disease and normalizes blood pressure
- Decreases overall cholesterol, and increase HDL – good cholesterol
- Anti-inflammatory properties
- Source of fiber – half soluble and half insoluble
- Counteracts iron deficiency and anemia
- Good for urinary tract infection and kidney stones
- Protects against osteoporosis, birth defects, and cognitive disorders
- Strong antioxidant properties

Note: Overall beet greens have a higher amount of nutrients than the beet roots. They are richer in iron, calcium, vitamin A and C, while the root is richer in manganese, potassium, fiber, and folic acid. Both are good sources of phosphorous, magnesium, and iron.

Broccoli: Many of the properties listed here are true for other cruciferous vegetables - broccoli just appears to be the superstar.
- **Lowers risk of cancer and helps to reverse cancer,** like other cruciferous vegetables it contains significant anticancer properties
- **Stops breast cancer cell proliferation – including cancer in estrogen sensitive breast cells**

- **Contains a substance that increases the body's cancer protective abilities**
- **Suppresses breast tumor cell growth, as well as cancer cell metastasis**
- **Protects against cancer, especially breast, colon, prostate, stomach, lung, bladder, and ovary**
- **Helps clear carcinogenic substances quickly and has chemo preventative activity**
- Boosts the body's detoxification enzymes and supports liver detoxification
- Enhances the immune system
- Enhances your bodies ability to heal sun damaged skin
- Promotes gastrointestinal health
- Cardiovascular protective – reduces risk of high blood pressure and heart disease
- Prevents cataracts
- Good source of calcium and vitamin C – a combo that prevents osteoporosis
- Prevents birth defects – eat lots during pregnancy
- A good source for many nutrients, vitamins, and minerals

Brussels Sprouts: (See also broccoli)
- **Inhibits cancer**, especially colon and stomach
- High in protein, accounting for more than a quarter of its calories - the protein is incomplete, but it can be made complete when eaten with whole grains
- A good source of vitamin A, folacin, potassium, calcium, and vitamin C
- High in fiber, low in calories

Cabbage: (See also broccoli)
- **Lowers the risk of cancer, especially colon and stomach cancers**
- Stimulates the immune system
- Has antibacterial and antiviral properties
- Prevents and heals stomach ulcers

Carrots:
- **Blocks cancer**
- **Beneficial to blood sugar regulation**
- Lowers cholesterol and protects against cardiovascular disease
- Promotes better vision
- Prevents constipation; overall good for the stomach
- Support lung and colon health

Cauliflower: (See also broccoli)
- **Lowers the risk of cancer, especially colon and stomach**
- **Prevents breast cancer and other female cancers**
- Enhances cardiovascular health
- Supports the immune system
- A good source of vitamin C; three florets of cauliflower provide 67% of the daily requirement
- Improves colon health

Collard Greens: (See also broccoli)
- Lowers the risk of cognitive decline
- Aids detoxification
- **Prevents risk of cancer – especially colon cancer**
- Provides immune system support
- Provides cardiovascular support, including lowering cholesterol

- Prevents osteoporosis – a good source of calcium
- Contains antioxidant properties
- Promotes healthy lungs

Kale: (See also broccoli)
- **Boosts the body's detoxification enzymes to clear carcinogenic matter**
- **Blocks many types of cancer – stops breast cancer cell proliferation**
- Abundant in calcium, lutein, iron, vitamins A, C, K, E, and beta-carotene
- Promotes lung health
- Enhances the immune system
- Good source of calcium - prevents osteoporosis
- Good source of fiber
- Contains antioxidant properties
- Enhances overall energy
- Supports a healthy nervous system
- Good for the eyes - prevents cataracts from forming

Mustard Greens:
- **Anticancer properties**
- **Protects against breast cancer**
- **Supports the liver to reduce potential carcinogens**
- Reduces the symptoms of menopause
- Provides antioxidant protection
- Promotes overall heart health, including preventing heart disease
- Rich in calcium, magnesium, and folic acid to support healthy bones; source of fiber
- Supports healthy lungs and helps to heal asthma
- Helps to prevent rheumatoid arthritis

Onion:
- Natural antibiotic properties
- Good for the heart; lowering cholesterol, regulating blood pressure, and preventing heart disease
- Prevents blood clotting and thins blood
- Anti-inflammatory properties
- Regulates blood sugar
- Antibacterial properties
- Relieves colds, coughs, asthma, and bronchial congestion
- **Prevents cancer and tumor growth, especially in the stomach and colon**
- Red onions also have antioxidant benefits

Radish: This was not part of my healing journey, but I have recently added this to my diet for variety and for the health benefits. I eat it raw, as part of a raw drink or salad, or cooked with other vegetables/foods. It is a low alkaline food, but it is a little spicy, so I only eat it occasionally.
- Source of vitamin A, C, calcium, potassium, and other nutrients
- **Contains cancer preventative properties**
- Good for weight management - very low in calories, yet filling due to its fiber and water content.
- Treats free radical damage improving the health of your skin, slowing aging
- Good for type 1 and 2 diabetes and liver disorders
- Aids respiratory disorders like asthma, bronchitis, coughs, colds, and flu
- Improves digestion and assists with digestive issues, including constipation

- Has diuretic properties
- Helps to dissolve gallstones and kidney stones; prevents urinary infections

Romaine Lettuce:
- **Helps to prevent colon cancer**
- A good source of dietary fiber and other vitamins and minerals such as of vitamin A, K, and C, calcium, potassium, folic acid, chromium, and manganese
- Enhances bone strength, reducing the risk of osteoporosis
- Assists with weight loss and aids digestion
- Enhances heart health - prevents oxidation of cholesterol, lowers cholesterol levels, lowers high blood pressure, and reduces the risk of heart attack

Scallion:
- It includes allicin, which has benefits such as lowering cholesterol and promoting a healthy heart
- **Lowers the risk of some cancers**
- An anticoagulant that keeps the blood flowing and free of clots
- Effective in stimulating sweat, aids urination, and calms nerves
- Expels sputum – mucus or phlegm coughed up from the lower airways
- Used to treat fungal infections, bacterial infections, sinus infections, and colds

Spinach:
- **Reduces the risk of cancer -** A and C vitamins, plus the fiber, folic acid, magnesium, and other nutrients help control cancer, especially colon, prostate, lung, breast, and ovarian cancers
- Good calcium and vitamin K content – strengthens bones
- Protects against heart disease and stroke; lowers cholesterol
- Its flavonoids protect against memory loss
- Helps to prevent cataracts and blindness

Squash: Winter (orange) varieties including acorn, butternut, and pumpkin.
- **Lowers risk of cancer**
- **Reduces risk of colon cancer**; promotes colon health
- Good source of fiber
- Overall good for the stomach
- Prevents prostate problems
- Aids healthy lungs – **lowers risk of lung cancer** (if you know a smoker who won't stop, encourage the addition of foods such as winter squash and carrots that are rich in vitamin A)
- Contains many nutrients: beta-carotene, C, B1, B6, B3, manganese, potassium, foliate, dietary fiber, pantothenic acid, and copper
- Provides antioxidant and anti-inflammatory properties
- Helps to prevent cholesterol, heart attacks, and strokes; lowers blood pressure
- Provides blood sugar regulation
- Reduces asthma, osteoarthritis, and rheumatoid arthritis

Turnip:
- **Prevents cancer**
- Contains diuretic properties
- High in vitamin C and fiber
- Contains folic acid, manganese, niacin, vitamin E, and potassium

- Strong antioxidant
- Aids in iron absorption

Turnip Greens:
- **Prevents cancer**
- Good source of vitamins A, C, E, B6, and K, calcium, manganese, copper, and fiber
- Rich in folic acid – important for the growth and maintenance of all cells
- Minimizes LDL (bad) cholesterol oxidation
- Relieves the pain of rheumatoid arthritis
- Slows the loss of cognitive functioning
- Supports intestinal health – especially the colon
- Supports healthy lungs
- Prevents skin problems and eye disorders
- Supports healthy bones – a good source of calcium and magnesium

Yam / Sweet Potato:
- Fairly low in calories and have no fat, while rich in beta-carotene and potassium
- Stabilizes blood sugar levels
- Protects against heart attacks, prevents heart disease, maintains the fluid and electrolyte balance in the cells, normal heart function, and blood pressure
- **Lowers risk of cancer, especially lung cancer**
- Antioxidant and anti-inflammatory properties
- Wild yams have anti-weight gain, **anticancer,** and anti-aging properties

Beans / Lentils

This category includes black-eyed peas, split peas, chickpeas, kidney beans, lentils, lima beans, pinto beans, white beans, black beans, etc. When combined with rice, beans and lentils are a complete protein.
- Great source of soluble fiber and protein, yet low in fat
- Contains iron, calcium, folic acid, copper, and magnesium
- **Inhibits cancer**
- Controls insulin and blood sugar; protects against type 2 diabetes
- Reduces bad cholesterol (LDL)
- Lowers blood pressure; prevents heart disease and strokes
- Regulates the colon, prevents and treats constipation, hemorrhoids, and other bowel problems
- Source of omega-3

Hummus: It is usually made from chickpeas (also called garbanzos), tahini, garlic, olive oil, lemon juice, and sea salt. It has great benefits from all of its ingredients, in addition to what is listed below. (Also, see the 'Recipe' section, page 89, for simple ideas on how to make it at home.)
- Rich in nutrients, especially folic acid, manganese, tryptophan, copper, iron, and zinc
- Source of healthy protein
- Low GI - glycemic index
- Helps prevent diabetes
- Promotes relaxation and restful sleep
- Rich in fiber – helps lower cholesterol and regulate blood sugar levels
- Lowers risk of heart disease

Traditional Sources of Protein:

Fish: I eat white flake fish and salmon only. Other fish and shellfish can hold onto microorganisms and mercury. Farm fed fish such as salmon and tilapia may contain hormones. Buy wild caught fish.
- **Prevents cancer**
- Good source of protein with fewer calories and fat than most protein sources
- Anticoagulant and blood thinner; protects arteries from damage
- Reduces blood triglycerides and harmful LDL cholesterol
- Lowers blood pressure, and reduces risk of heart attack and stroke
- Enhances mental functioning and memory
- Anti-inflammatory properties - reduces symptoms of rheumatoid arthritis
- Minimizes migraine headaches; eases bronchial asthma; fights kidney disease
- Provides immune system support
- Salmon is a good source of omega-3 and vitamin D (especially sockeye salmon)

Eggs: Organic, with hormone free feed.
- **May lower the risk of breast cancer**
- One egg contains about six grams of high-quality protein, all nine essential amino acids, and vitamins, minerals, protein, and energy – all for only about 68 calories
- Contains healthy fat and is low in saturated fat and contains naturally occurring vitamin D
- Contains lutein and zeaxanthin, for healthy eyes, lowers the risk of developing cataracts
- Prevents blood clotting, strokes, and heart attacks
- A good source of choline, which helps to regulate the brain, nervous system, cardiovascular system, and reduces inflammation
- Promotes healthy teeth, bones, nails, and hair
- Supports the immune system and the functioning of the brain including memory
- Moderate consumption of eggs does not negatively impact cholesterol levels or cause heart disease

Yogurt: Plain and organic is recommended.
- Contains the good bacteria needed for your intestines – promotes stomach health
- Prevents and treats intestinal infections and diarrhea; improves bowel functioning
- **Provides anticancer activity**
- Kills bacteria and enhances the immune system - may prevent vaginal infections
- Lowers LDL (harmful) cholesterol and reduces high blood pressure
- A source of protein and calcium – prevents osteoporosis

Non-traditional Sources of Protein:

My Alternative Protein Sources:
- Miso, Tamari, and Tempeh - fermented soy foods
- Beans and Lentils - complete protein if added with grains
- Hummus
- Seeds and Nuts
- Quinoa (grain)
- Avocado - limited protein
- Brussels Sprouts - complete protein if added with grains
- Royal Jelly - 1/2 this supplement's dry weight is protein

Soy:
Use caution with unfermented soy. Choose fermented soy products! Why?

Unfermented soy contains:
- Trypsin Inhibitor - reduces your ability to digest protein
- Nitrites that are potent carcinogens
- May contain MSG
- Goitrogens - depress the function of thyroid, may eventually cause thyroid cancer
- Phytic acid - blocks the absorption of key minerals like iron, calcium, copper, and zinc in the intestinal tract
- Phyto-estrogens – a probable factor in breast cancer and infantile leukemia
- Unfermented soy may accelerate growth of tumors

There are articles and studies that suggest that unfermented soy is generally unsafe, especially for infants and children. Please do your own research to make informed eating decisions.

Fermented Foods - Ensures Intestinal Health & More!

The term fermented may conjure up images of distasteful food. I know I gave this type of food little consideration until I was on my self-healing journey with breast cancer and parasites.

I learned that fermented foods not only taste good, but they are good for the stomach and the body too. These foods are extremely beneficial to your overall health.

Some fermented foods are considered natural probiotics and all fermented foods promote good bacteria in your stomach, supporting the proper digestion of nutrients. These foods also have properties that promote the effective functioning of your immune system. They help increase the levels of B vitamins, digestive enzymes, omega-3 acids, and other properties in your body that combat bad bacteria and **even cancer cells.**

Fermented Foods that I Include in My Diet:
- *Organic Sauerkraut:* available both raw and cooked
- *Miso:* a fermented soy paste that contains enzymes that aid digestion
- *Tempeh:* made by the fermentation of cooked soybeans
- *Tamari:* a fermented condiment similar to soy sauce that is healthier for you
- *Komboucha:* a living raw drink with many health benefits
- *Umeboshi:* a pickled plum, which is also available as a paste

Sauerkraut: Organic sauerkraut is expensive so I use it as a condiment, one to two tablespoons with a meal or in between meals, up to four or five times per week. It is available in both raw and cooked forms; raw is preferred but cooked is acceptable. I recently started making my own sauerkraut with organic raw green cabbage and sea salt. It is easy to do and much less expensive.
- **Has anticancer properties - reduces risk of breast, lung, liver, colon, and prostate cancers**
- Boosts the immune system
- Protects the balance of your gastrointestinal tract by adding healthy bacteria
- Aids in digestion and the breakdown of proteins
- Creates a soothing effect to the nervous system
- Helps fight the flu

Miso: A fermented soybean paste with a texture similar to peanut butter, and a strong salty flavor. It is used as a condiment and a flavoring agent to make the popular miso soup.

- Contains vitamin B-12 and trace minerals including zinc, manganese, and copper
- A protein source -- one tablespoon has two grams of protein and just 25 calories
- **Helps reduce the risk of cancer of the breast, prostate, lung, and colon**
- **Regulates estrogen in women - a hormone that causes tumors to develop**
- **Prevents and clears your body of radiation**
- Releases and blocks heavy metals; eliminates tobacco poisoning
- Enhances the immune system, bones, and overall energy
- Helps prevent heart disease and protects blood vessels
- A strong antioxidant – enhancing skin health and counteracting the aging process
- Reduces chronic pain and menopause pain
- Aids digestion and intestinal health; heals poor digestion and intestinal infections
- Balances acidic conditions in the gastrointestinal tract

Note: Miso is high in sodium, so it may not be appropriate for those on low-sodium diets.

Tempeh: Tempeh has a firm texture and a nutty flavor. It may be cooked in a number of ways, but it is most commonly sliced and pan-fried until the surface is crisp and golden brown. Tempeh can be used in soups, spreads, salads, and more.

- A complete protein that is rich in fiber, and contains many essential amino acids, manganese, copper, magnesium, and riboflavin
- **Reduces the risk of some cancers, such as prostate and colon**
- Provides digestive benefits and supports a healthy gastrointestinal tract
- Contains health promoting phytochemicals that reduce heart disease, strengthen bones, and eases menopause symptoms
- Lowers LDL (bad) cholesterol and raises HDL (good) cholesterol

Note: Avoid eating tempeh in large quantities if you have a history of kidney stones.

Tamari Soy Sauce: Like miso, tamari is a fermented soy food, and it shares many of miso's health and nutritional properties (see above).

- A seasoning alternative to salt that contains protein, niacin, manganese, and tryptophan - which is critical for nitrogen balance and the production of serotonin
- Does not contain wheat - an excellent seasoning for those on a wheat free diet
- **Has strong anticancer** and antioxidant properties
- Aids in the digestion of grains and vegetables

Komboucha: An organic raw living drink. I like komboucha with ginger. I get the added benefits of ginger and it tastes good.

- Includes enzymes, probiotics, and detoxifiers
- Supports digestion and healthy intestinal environment
- Enhances the immune system
- Supports metabolism, helps appetite control, and aids in weight loss
- Supports liver function
- Aids in body alignment, restores balance and vitality
- Anti-aging properties and improves cell integrity
- Supports healthy skin and hair

Umeboshi: Pickled plums have a very strong taste and are salty. I use one round teaspoon as a condiment with a meal, several times a week.
- Purifies blood, revitalizes the body, and prevents aging
- Has an alkalizing effect on the body
- Good for stomach health
- Prevents and minimizes fatigue
- Relieves migraine headaches
- Stimulates digestion and facilitates the elimination of toxins
- Cure for a hangover

Healing Fruits

This section includes fruits that support your stomach's alkaline balance, supports intestinal health, compliments a macrobiotic diet, and are not overly high in natural sugars.

When buying dried fruits, check the label to make sure that sugar or cane syrup was not added. Fruits are naturally sweet so the extra sugar is not needed. Sugar may cultivate an environment that could breed yeast, bacteria, parasites, cancer, and more.

Apple:
- Good for the heart: antioxidants, flavonoids, fiber (soluble and insoluble) - lowers cholesterol, blood pressure, and the risk of heart disease
- Stabilizes blood sugar, suppresses appetite, and good for overall stomach health
- **Has properties that block cancer, especially breast, lung, and colon cancers**
- Diluted apple cider vinegar with honey helps to heal bladder infections
- Diluted apple cider vinegar balances an upset/gassy stomach
- High in digestible antioxidants, especially Red Delicious and Granny Smith varieties
- Anti-allergenic, anti-carcinogenic, anti-inflammatory, antiviral, and anti-proliferative

Apricot: (dried)
- **A cancer inhibitor**, especially for cancer of the lung, pancreas, and larynx; recommended for smokers and ex-smokers
- Rich in beta-carotene and a good source of vitamin A, C, and E, iron, and potassium
- Good fiber content, aiding digestion
- Promotes healthy eyesight and prevents heart disease
- Antioxidant content supports the immune system
- Weight control: an apricot contains approximately 17 calories

Avocado:
- **Protects against breast, prostate, and oral cancers**
- Promotes heart health: prevents strokes and heart disease, reduces LDL cholesterol, increases HDL cholesterol, regulates blood pressure, and helps circulatory problems
- Helps to control weight
- A source of fiber and antioxidants
- Heals digestive problems
- Maintains healthy eyes and healthy skin, while preventing wrinkles

Blueberry: Dried or fresh
- **Prevents and fights cancer, especially ovarian and colon**
- Heals diarrhea (especially dried blueberries) and constipation; good for overall intestinal health
- High in digestible antioxidants, supporting the immune system
- Lowers cholesterol and protects blood vessels from damage
- Fights osteoporosis
- Antiviral properties; prevents urinary tract infection
- Improves brain function and improves memory
- Improves vision, including night vision
- Supports weight loss and better sleep

Cherry: Preferably dried
- **Prevents and fights cancer,** heart disease, diabetes, and rheumatoid arthritis
- A good source of digestible antioxidants
- Prevents cavities
- Relieves the pain of arthritis and gout; provides overall pain relief
- Rich source of melatonin which regulates sleep patterns, slows aging and memory loss

Cranberry: This is not part of my diet, but I have included it in this book as it helps remedy urinary infections. I would use it as a 'medicine' when needed since it is highly acidic.
- Provides antibacterial, antiviral, and anti-inflammatory properties
- Prevents and heals urinary tract infections
- Prevents kidney stones, gum disease, and strokes

Lemon & Lime:
- **Blocks cancer**
- Contains cleansing, detoxing, balancing properties - squeeze a little in a glass of water each day
- Although lemon and lime taste acidic, when consumed they are alkalizing
- Soothes heart burn and aids digestion
- Anti-inflammatory and antiviral – good for colds, sore throats, and asthma

Pear:
- **Protects women against post-menopausal breast cancer**
- Provides antioxidant protection
- Ensures regularity of bowel movement and good for overall colon health
- Lowers cholesterol levels and blood pressure; prevents strokes
- Anti-inflammatory properties
- Supports kidney functioning
- Reduces the risk of osteoporosis by retaining calcium

Raisin:
- **Prevents cancer, especially colon cancer; prevents tumor growth**
- Antioxidant properties
- Beneficial for teeth, gums, and eyes
- Good source of energy
- Enhances density of bones and lowers occurrence of osteoporosis
- Good source of fiber – helps counteract constipation
- Protects against heart disease; promotes cardiovascular health

Super Berries:

These are just two of the super berries that are now available to us. I choose these for their health benefits and ease of availability compared to some of the rarer berries. They usually can be found as dried fruit or concentrated juice.

Acai Berry:
- Improves digestive functioning
- Boosts energy levels, improves mental clarity and focus
- Provides potent antioxidant activity
- Contains high levels of fiber
- Cleanses and detoxifies the body of toxins
- Strengthens the immune system
- **Fights cancer cells**
- Slows down the aging process; promotes healthier and younger-looking skin
- Alleviates diabetes
- Helps maintain healthy heart function; improves circulation; regulates cholesterol levels
- Minimizes inflammation and relieves arthritis pain
- Enhances visual clarity

Goji Berry:
- Contains high levels of antioxidants and detoxifying enzymes
- **Prevents and fights cancer**
- Boosts energy and enhances mood
- Improves melatonin levels, aiding in restful sleep
- Increases metabolism
- Enhances the libido
- Lowers cholesterol and blood pressure
- Defends against inflammatory free-radicals
- Increases white blood cells needed for immune defense
- Enhances mental acuity, the ability to focus, and vision - anti-aging properties
- Supports hormone balance in women

Grains: These are a Healthy Surprise!

Barley:
- Source of antioxidants, protein, calcium, magnesium, phosphorus, selenium, potassium, and lutein
- Lowers cholesterol - promotes heart health
- **Inhibits cancer; prevents colon and breast cancer**
- Improves bowel functioning; relieves constipation
- Fights type 2 diabetes and pre-diabetes

Brown Rice:
- Lowers blood pressure; regulates cholesterol, and promotes healthy heart
- Fights diarrhea; overall good for the stomach
- Prevents kidney stones
- Clears psoriasis; supports healthy skin, nail, hair, teeth, bones, and muscles
- **Prevents cancer**
- Regulates blood sugar - good for diabetes

Millet:
- Non-acid forming food, gluten free, soothing and easy to digest
- Nearly 15% protein and fiber rich
- Lowers cholesterol and blood pressure
- **Reduces the risk of cancer**
- Contains B-complex vitamins, amino acid methionine, lecithin, and vitamin E
- High in iron, magnesium, phosphorus, and potassium
- Addresses type 2 diabetes, migraine headaches, and asthma

Quinoa: Considered a super grain that can supply all of the body's requirements, carbohydrates, fats, protein, vitamins, minerals, and fiber.
- Gluten free and easy to digest
- Quinoa is 12-22% protein - a complete protein with all of the essential amino acids
- Good source of fiber, phosphorus, magnesium, iron, and B vitamins
- One cup of quinoa has the same calcium content as a quart of milk, yet because it is from a plant it is easily absorbed and better quality
- **Combats cancer and protects against breast cancer**
- Eliminates migraine headaches
- Supports muscle health and overall physical health
- Promotes cardiovascular health and prevents heart failure
- Provides antioxidant protection
- Prevents gallstones

Nuts & Seeds - a Source of Protein & Fiber

Almonds:
- 90% of its fat is unsaturated
- **Prevents cancer**
- Lowers cholesterol – 3 oz of almonds daily, can lower cholesterol up to 14%
- Regulates blood sugar and lowers the risk of diabetes
- A source of protein, fiber, calcium, magnesium, potassium, vitamin E, selenium, zinc, copper, potassium, phosphorus, biotin, riboflavin, niacin, and iron
- Helps prevent osteoporosis

Brazil Nuts:
- High levels of selenium and all of the amino acids make this protein 'complete'
- A powerful antioxidant linked to **lower rates of cancer** and heart disease
- A good source of zinc, needed for digestion, metabolism, and immune system functioning

Note: These nuts contain high amounts of fat. These fats are unsaturated and are healthy if eaten in small amounts. Most sources recommend about seven nuts per serving, three times a week to limit the amount of fat.

Pumpkin Seeds: Recommend raw and unsalted.
- **Prevents and protects against cancer**
- Prevents and lowers cholesterol
- Has anti-inflammatory properties
- Helpful to prostate problems; relieves urination difficulties associated with an enlarged prostate
- Improves bladder function and prevents kidney stones

- Beneficial to skin hair, nails, teeth, gums, and nerves
- Contains L-tryptophan, effective against depression
- Source of calcium and magnesium - good for preventing osteoporosis
- A great source of magnesium – 1/2 cup contains 92% of your daily requirement
- Remedy for parasites and tapeworms; relieves constipation

Sesame Seeds / Sesame Oil:
- **Is a chemo-preventive agent**
- **Helps to prevent colon cancer**
- Prevents osteoporosis: 1/2 cup has three times more calcium than 1/2 cup of whole milk
- Contains manganese, copper, magnesium, iron, phosphorus, vitamin B1, zinc, vitamin E, and iron
- Contains healthy protein, fiber, and antioxidant benefits
- Prevents high blood pressure; lowers cholesterol; and enhances overall cardiovascular health
- Protects against liver damage and supports the kidneys
- Prevents dry skin or skin problems; external application diminishes wrinkles
- Reduces osteoporosis, migraine headaches, and rheumatoid arthritis

Walnuts: I moderately added walnuts to my diet while editing this book. They have amazing benefits!
- **Helps to prevent cancer cells from replicating**
- Provides antioxidant protection
- Improves cognitive functioning; a source of brain and memory support
- A source of melatonin which enables a good night's sleep
- Rich in omega-3 which protect bone health and more
- Lowers cholesterol levels; prevents heart attacks; controls blood pressure; and aids a healthy heart
- Regulates blood sugar levels; improves type 2 diabetes
- Contains anti-inflammatory properties
- Prevents gallstones and provides liver support
- Prevents weight gain and helps improve metabolism

Seasonings, Oils, Seaweed, & Miscellaneous

Garlic:
- Antibiotic properties; fights infections; treatment for the common cold
- **Prevents cancer – especially breast, stomach, prostate, and bladder; reduces tumors**
- Thins blood, prevents blood clots, lowers blood pressure, and regulates cholesterol
- Supports the immune system
- Acts as a expectorant and decongestant:, prevents and relieves bronchitis

Ginger:
- Aids digestion and the pH balance of the stomach - helps to relieve cramping, nausea, and diarrhea
- Use as a tea to relieve heartburn, morning and motion sickness, and menstrual cramps
- **Prevents cancer - especially ovarian and colon cancer; reduces tumors**
- Thins blood, lowers cholesterol, and speeds metabolic rate
- Anti-inflammatory and a natural pain killer
- Good for treating colds and sore throats

Natural Honey:
- Alleviates asthma and soothes sore throats

- Prevents and relieves chronic bronchitis
- Calms nerves and promotes sleep
- Treats colds, stomachaches, and diarrhea
- Has antibacterial and antioxidant properties
- Honey, along with diluted apple cider vinegar taken every hour, may heal bladder infections
- Boosts energy levels and the immune system

Borage Oil: See 'Supplement' section, page 68.

Flax Seed Oil: See 'Supplement' section, page 68.

Olive Oil:
- Promotes a healthy heart, lowers blood pressure, and thins blood
- Reduces bad LDL cholesterol and raises good HDL cholesterol
- **Prevents cancer, especially colon cancer**
- Contains a high content of antioxidant substances - slows aging

Sesame Seeds / Sesame Oil: See page 65.

Seaweed: Including kelp, nori, and wakame. Seaweed does not need to be taken in large quantities for the benefits. 1/4 sheet of nori shredded on rice or vegetables once a day or a few small pieces of wakame in your miso soup, vegetables, or rice is fine. Currently I use a pinch of kelp powder in my green smoothies every three days, to make sure that my iodine level is maintained. During my journey, I took it every day.
- **Blocks cancer** and enhances the immune system
- Promotes detoxification of the body, including heavy metals
- Lowers blood cholesterol and blood pressure, prevents strokes and thins blood
- Increases metabolism and overall vitality
- Prevents osteoporosis, kills bacteria, and heals stomach ulcers
- A source of iodine, important for thyroid functioning
- Contains a wide range of minerals, trace minerals, vitamins, fiber, phytonutrients, antioxidants, essential fatty acids, and nucleic acids

Wine: Red is preferred for health benefits, but the benefits exist only when used in moderation. I was alcohol free during my healing journey. Now I have an occasional glass of wine.
- Contains antioxidant properties - kills bacteria and viruses
- Prevents heart disease and raises good HDL cholesterol
- **Has chemicals that prevent cancer and reduces tumors**
- Slows neurological degenerative disorders

Some risks of drinking wine:
- **Increases the risk of breast cancer, especially estrogen positive breast cancer**
- Raises blood pressure levels; contributes to diabetes
- Contributes to migraine headaches and weight gain

Culinary Herbs & Spices

Allspice:
- Aids digestion, relieves stomach aches and indigestion
- Relieves colds and provides mild pain relief – effective at easing arthritis and sore muscles

- Contains antifungal and antiseptic substances
- Regulates blood sugar levels

Basil:
- One of a few herbs that was included in my macrobiotic diet
- **Protects against radiation damage**
- **Protects against most types of cancer**, cellular aging, and skin problems
- Blocks damage to cells and the oxidization of cholesterol
- Treatment for respiratory problems and allergies, when combined with honey and ginger tea
- Basil's essential oil inhibits several types of bacteria - helpful if they become resistant to antibiotics
- The essential oil has an anti-inflammatory effect, aiding rheumatoid arthritis and other conditions
- Aids heart health and improves blood flow

Bay Leaf:
- One of a few herbs that was included in my macrobiotic diet
- Helps digestive disorders and rheumatism
- Has antibacterial and antifungal properties

Cilantro:
- A good cleansing and alkaline herb
- Works as a natural chelation therapy for excess metals
- Clears infections (viral and bacterial) especially when eaten with omega-3 foods
- Regulates blood sugar, cholesterol, and eases inflammation
- Contains antimicrobial properties

Cinnamon:
- **Reduces the growth of leukemia and lymphoma cancer cells**
- Helps to treat colds, headaches, and toothaches
- Improves colon health: provides relief from diarrhea, constipation, and IBS
- Lowers LDL cholesterol (studies suggest 1/2 tsp daily); prevents heart disease
- Stops yeast infections and the growth of bacteria and fungus
- Anticoagulant properties
- Has anti-inflammatory properties; relieves arthritis pain
- Enhances memory and overall brain functioning
- Regulates blood sugar; beneficial for type 2 diabetes

Oregano:
- Has strong antibacterial, antifungal, and antibiotic properties
- An effective killer of food borne microbes and pathogens
- Oil of oregano combats parasites, improves respiratory health, and enhances the immune system
- A source of many antioxidants and vitamins, **helping to prevent cancer** and slow aging
- An antioxidant dense food - 1 tablespoon of fresh oregano is equal to a medium apple
- Treats athlete's foot, psoriasis, and eczema

Note: Avoid oregano in large quantities if pregnant or nursing.

Rosemary:
- One of a few herbs that was included in my macrobiotic diet
- Assists with stomach upsets, digestive disorders, and headaches
- **Helps prevent cancer** and age related skin damage

- Contains effective antioxidant and anti-inflammatory properties
- Boosts liver function and the immune system
- Counteracts fatigue - drink as a tea
- Improves circulations and blood flow to the head and brain

Thyme:
- One of a few herbs that was included in my macrobiotic diet
- **Contains anticancer properties**
- Ability to expel parasites
- Provides antioxidant protection of cell membranes, especially in brain, kidney, and heart cells
- Provides antimicrobial activity against bacteria and fungus
- Good for bronchitis, cough, chest congestion, and respiratory tract inflammation

Turmeric / Cumin:
- **Fights cancer in all stages; has antitumor properties**
- **Prevents breast cancer from spreading**
- **When combined with cauliflower, prevents and stops prostate cancer**
- **Prevents metastases from occurring in cancer**
- **Boosts the effects of chemo drug paclitaxel while reducing its side effects**
- **Stops the growth of new blood vessels in tumors**
- Detoxifies and protects the liver
- Balances cholesterol levels; protects the heart
- Has antiseptic, antibacterial, and antioxidant properties
- A natural anti-inflammatory – good for arthritis, rheumatoid arthritis, and joint pain
- Helps psoriasis and other inflammatory skin conditions
- Fights allergies and enhances the immune system
- Helps to fight and prevent parasites and gallstones
- Aids and stimulates digestion - supports a healthy stomach
- A natural pain killer; supports weight management
- Chinese medicine uses it as a treatment for depression

Healing Supplements Including Medicinal Herbs & Herbal Teas

During my healing journey, I included many foods, herbs, teas, and supplements to support my body. This section is about those items that were added to complement my diet and enhance my healing. They include plant or herbal based supplements, special teas, and more. I never took any medicines - prescription or over the counter. I buy many of my supplements, vitamins, minerals, etc, on the internet.

I suggest that you do your own research and consult with experts that can guide you in the right direction for your health. Please take special consideration if you have any allergies, serious disease, or are pregnant or nursing.

Supplements:

• **Oxy E:** In order to heal and maintain health our cells need to be fully oxygenated. Although I was doing physical activities to oxygenate like yoga, Pilates, and breath work, I wanted to make sure that I had high levels of oxygen for my cells. I added this liquid supplement to my routine within the first week, putting six drops into every glass of water that I drank. As a preventative step – take 10 minutes a day to just sit and breathe from your belly and if you want an extra boost take six drops of *Oxy E* once a day or every other day. *Oxy E* is primarily an ionic mineral solution with fulvic acid, and trace amounts of other vitamins, minerals, and amino acids.

• **Flax Seeds / Oil:** A good source of omega-3s, which are critical to cell health. The seeds have the added benefit of containing heart healthy fiber and lignan, a type of phytoestrogen (antioxidant) which plays a role in **preventing diseases such as breast cancer**. Buy ground or milled flaxseed, if you can find it. Alternatively, you can grind your own using a coffee grinder. When the seeds are not ground, your system is not able to fully digest them, so your body cannot harness the nutrients. A tablespoon of ground flaxseed is the recommended daily dose. Sprinkle on your cereal, salads, grains, and soups.

Why is omega-3 important? Omega-3 and omega-6 fatty acids are critical in the structure of cell membranes and the development of the nervous system. They form the foundation for the synthesis of cell mediators. These cell mediators play an important role in our health and can affect coagulation, inflammation, and production of certain cells.

The problem is that the typical American diet lacks the proper proportions of omega-3 to omega-6 fatty acids. Omega-6s are more easily found through our diets and if they are not balanced by 3s, it could cause inflammation and health issues for our body. The ratio of omega-6s to 3s should be somewhere between 2:1 and 4:1. In most diets, that ratio is between 10:1 and 30:1. This has serious implications for heart disease, cancer, arthritis, allergies, and other chronic diseases. It is important to maintain the proper balance for your health and well-being.

• **Trace Minerals:** There are so many trace minerals that our body needs, yet it is difficult to find them all, even in the best diet. When I was healing, I was trying to provide all that my body needed through foods, but I had to offset the fact that much of what I ate was not being digested. Therefore, I used *Concentrace Trace Mineral Drops,* adding a few drops of this liquid concentrate to my drinking water once a day. They are a little salty, but I add them to a small glass of water to get it out of the way quickly. I still use them today and add a few drops to my dog's drinking water. She deserves the best too.

• **Blue Green Algae:** Great for cleansing toxins, **heavy metals, and radiation from the body**. Repairs free radical damage, promotes healing of ulcers and wounds, reduces cholesterol, lowers LDL levels, stabilizes blood sugar levels, strengthens the immune system, increases energy, and so much more. I took this powdered supplement daily while I was healing, for immune support and cleansing. I still take the blue green algae three times a week.

• **CoQ10:** It plays a key role in producing energy in our body's cells and is a key ingredient of every cell. CoQ10 is a popular supplement for anti-aging. I took 400mg daily while healing, which I have slowly reduced to a capsule of 100mg, in order to maintain my cells and support my body's energy.

• **DIM:** DIM is a phytonutrient that is found in cruciferous vegetables. It promotes healthy estrogen metabolism. Why is that important? Estrogen production is associated with certain types of cancer. **You can reduce the risk of cancer or help to heal it, by improving your estrogen metabolism**. This can be accomplished through diet with cruciferous vegetables, omega-3, and lignans in foods like flaxseed. DIM isolates a single compound from cruciferous vegetables that promotes a beneficial change in the metabolism of estrogen. This change greatly reduces estrogen over-exposure by restoring and maintaining a favorable balance of estrogen metabolites. An optimal estrogen balance has positive implications for cancer prevention, aging in women and men, skin, bones, and prostate tissue in men. It also protects against cancer and heart disease, while promoting weight loss. Even though I was eating a diet high in cruciferous vegetables, I took a DIM capsule supplement because so much research has been done on its anticancer properties. Today, this is obtained solely through my diet.

- **Broccoli Extract:** If you do not like broccoli and are dealing with breast cancer, you can get broccoli extract pills to get the benefits from this power food. I was eating broccoli regularly, but I wanted the extra support, so I added the supplement as well.

- **Artemisinin:** A plant derived supplement that is good for **eliminating tumors and parasites**. It has a long history as a Chinese herbal.

- **Living Fuel:** A powdered multiple vitamin, when mixed with water provides a drink that is easily absorbed by your body. If you choose another supplement source, make sure that it is easily absorbed by your body. At first, I was taking a lot of pills, so I began to find more of my supplements in powder and extract form so I could add them to special drinks and smoothies. I used *Living Fuel* because it provided me a protein source and was my version of a daily multi-vitamin. It is a little pricey, but has many health benefits.

- **Royal Jelly:** A bee created substance that is also referred to as 'bee's milk'. I take this supplement in natural form – royal jelly mixed with honey. I added this towards the end of my journey for energy, adrenal support, and for a natural source of vitamin B complex. One spoonful daily enhances stamina, immunity, and longevity, along with having anti-inflammatory and **antitumor properties.** Specifically, it supplies all of the B-vitamins, vitamins A, C, D, E, and K, over 12 key minerals, 18 amino acids, and includes nucleic acids (DNA and RNA). With up to half of its dry weight being protein, it is an unusual protein source and contains several beneficial fatty acids.

- **Magnesium:** Magnesium, vitamin D, a calcium bone booster complex, and zinc are my tools for healthy bones. Magnesium is hard to absorb, and it is needed in order for calcium to be properly absorbed. My research showed that the common recommended balance of 400mg magnesium to 1000mg calcium might not be sufficient. Some suggest a much higher ratio, even as high as 1 to 1. It appears that if you have a higher level of magnesium more calcium can be absorbed, so you don't need to take as much calcium.

I choose a powdered magnesium supplement as a powder is more readily absorbed by the body. Even though my bone booster complex has magnesium, I take a scoop of my powdered magnesium supplement daily to ensure calcium absorption. As I am near the completion of this book, I learned that there might be a new product on the horizon, magnesium oil. This would be even better at supporting cell integrity and calcium absorption, when it becomes available, because it has a much better cellular absorption rate.

- **Shou Wu Chih:** A Chinese herbal liquid extract derived from several plant sources. I used this to support my metal detoxing. It is good for overall energy, which can become depleted during rigorous detoxification protocols. Shou Wu Chih replenishes the vital essence of the liver and kidneys, along with strengthening bones and tendons, creating healthier joints. It even counteracts fatigue, helps eye disorders, and tonifies, warms, and invigorates blood.

- **Borage Oil:** This is a late discovery for me. When I was using detoxification protocols for aluminum, my skin started breaking out like mad. It was one of the ways that the aluminum was releasing. After I completed the aluminum detox, the skin breakouts continued. I was advised that my skin was screaming for additional support. It made sense as all of my health issues were skin related. In addition to adding even more calcium and zinc to my diet, I incorporated borage oil to get more healthy essential fatty acids in my system. Its properties actually help skin conditions. For some people, the EFAs (Essential Fatty Acids) are more easily absorbed with borage oil, than flax seed oil.

Borage oil has many great benefits including having **anticancer properties**, supporting the **prevention of cancers,** and reducing the symptoms of rheumatoid arthritis. It reduces pain, joint stiffness, and inflammation. Helps to reduce skin dryness and keeps skin healthy, supple, and young looking. It may improve skin conditions like eczema and psoriasis. It has also been shown to reduce cholesterol, prevent heart disease, improve blood pressure imbalances, and prevent blood clotting. It even improves neurological functioning.

The Key to Supplement Absorption

Vitamin absorption is something that anyone who takes supplements should pay special attention to. What is the best vitamin format for the highest percentage of absorption; pills, capsules, tablets, soft gels, powders, or liquids? I mostly use powders and liquids, here is why.

The respected *Physician's Desk Reference* contains research which shows that only about 10% to 20% of the nutrients in vitamin pills are absorbed by the human body. The rest ends up as waste. It also states that absorption of liquid supplements can be as high as 98%. Other research shows that liquid supplements can be up to 10 times more effective than supplements in pill form. Powdered supplements that are mixed with water actually become a liquid.

It is generally felt that among pills, capsules, tablets, and soft gels, those with enteric coating offer the best absorption.

Additionally, pills, capsules, and tablets are made with many 'inactive' or binding ingredients that have no benefit for the body. Some 'inactive' ingredients can actually inhibit absorption, making it more difficult for the body to breakdown and absorb the active ingredients. On the flip side, liquids or powders that contain flavorings, sweeteners, suspending agents, and artificial preservatives should be avoided as well.

I suggest doing research to determine what is best for you. There are pros and cons to all supplement formats. Lifestyle is also a consideration. For instance, how easy is it for you to swallow multiple pills or mix powdered supplement(s) with water?

My experience after working with a holistic medical clinic was that I was deficient in certain vitamins, even though I was taking those vitamins in adequate amounts, but they were in tablet forms. To correct the deficiencies liquid and powdered supplements were recommended by the clinic. I chose to stop taking any supplements in tablet form. I take some enteric-coated capsules, but the rest are powders and liquids, many in dropper form. These supplement my main source of vitamins and minerals, which is a diet full of healthy, fresh organic foods.

It is always best to get your vitamins and minerals from whole foods. They are easier to digest and offer added benefits like containing a variety of nutrients. They provide fiber, which is important for digestion and helps prevent diseases such as cancer, diabetes, and heart disease. Whole foods also contain antioxidants, which prevent cell and tissue damage. If you depend on supplements rather than eating whole foods, you will miss many health benefits. It is important to note that it is possible to overdose on supplements, which is seldom the case with whole foods.

There are times when supplementation is key, such as vitamin D, which seldom occurs naturally in foods or calcium because the daily requirement is very large. On the other hand, perhaps you are like me and want the security of some supplementation. Regardless of what format you choose, please select brands that exclude non-nutritive additives such as binders, filler, coatings, as well as those that are free of sweeteners and flavorings. Pure supplements are always the best.

Medicinal Herbs, Teas, & More:
Be sure to use a trusted, organic source for all herbs and teas.

Bach Flower Essence's Rescue Remedy: I have had this in my pantry for years, and used it to calm myself when I learned of my diagnosis of cancer. A few drops under your tongue helps to create calm and alleviate stress at the moment that you need to be rescued. All *Bach Flower Essences* are from natural plant sources.

Calendula Flower Petals: My herbologist suggested that I steep this herb to use as a douche to support the healing of the displaced cells in my vagina. It is suitable for drinking by itself or adding with other teas. Calendula can be taken internally as a tea or used topically. Its health benefits include:
- Contains excellent anti-inflammatory and antibacterial properties.
- Very soothing and supportive of skin health. When applied topically heals skin irritations, wounds, bee stings, eczema, herpes, varicose veins, and athlete's foot – to name a few.
- Drinking calendula tea reduces bowel inflammation; heals colitis, stomach cramps, and menstrual discomfort; aids digestion, inflammatory pelvic disease, and stomach ulcers.
- Gargling with the cool tea relieves inflamed tonsils, sore throat, coughing, and canker sores.
- **Can prevent/heal dermatitis from radiation therapy.**
- Helpful in the treatment of HIV; may reduce blood pressure.
- Aids gallbladder and liver functioning.

Note: It is available as oil for topical treatment of skin disorders, and is often an ingredient in natural skin healing lotions.

California Poppy: During the first few weeks of my healing journey, I used an herbal tincture of california poppy when I needed help relaxing or had trouble sleeping.
- Calms nervousness and anxiousness – contains antispasmodic properties.
- Aids in relaxation and a restful nights sleep, while stabilizing psychological orientation.
- Supports pain relief; may help bed-wetting.

Chrysanthemum: It was recommended by my acupuncture doctor to help with the metal detoxing. I used a powder form, putting in warm water to drink as a tea.
- Commonly used in Chinese herbal formulas to neutralize toxins and protect the liver.
- Detoxifies the blood. Relieves sinus congestion and high blood pressure.
- Calms the nerves, and enhances vision, hearing, and mental alertness.

Combination Tea: I made a healing tea from three herbs, burdock root, red root, and oregon grape root. I buy these herbs in bulk, make the tea, and store in a one gallon jug. I drink one cup every few days. However, when I was healing, I drank about two cups a day. I started this routine while healing dysplasia of the vagina, but my herbologist suggested that it would help with the diagnosis of breast cancer too.

Burdock Root:
- Antibacterial and antifungal properties.
- Clears toxins from the blood stream and is an effective diuretic.
- Improves the function of elimination organs (liver, kidneys, and colon), enhancing overall body health.
- Functions as a diaphoretic, creating sweat, which is beneficial in neutralizing and eliminating toxins.
- It has a soothing effect on the gastrointestinal tract; supports digestion; used as a gentle laxative
- Supports healthy skin.
- Contains minerals such as iron, inulin (a helpful sugar for diabetics), and many trace minerals.

Red Root:
- Is a lymphatic cleanser; clears decongestion of lymphatic tissue, spleen, circulatory system, and liver.
- Enhances the body's ability to carry cellular waste away from infected areas.
- Aids asthma, bronchitis, sore throat, headache, fever, and fatigue.
- **Breaks up ovarian and breast cysts, and tumors.**

Oregon Grape Root:
- Protects against bacteria, viruses, and fungi - stimulates the immune system.
- Treats bacterial diarrhea, intestinal parasites, and eye infections.
- Relieves digestive tract irritation including, stomach cramps and abdominal pain, and stimulates digestion.
- Supports healthy liver functioning.
- Good for skin problems, reduces inflammation of the skin and arthritis.

Dandelion Tea:
- Chinese medicine uses it to boost chi, or positive energy in the body.
- Helps to purify blood and cleanse the body's system; improves skin health and appearance.
- Contains many vitamins and minerals.
- Enhances detoxification through urination, while replacing lost potassium.
- A natural expectorant - helpful for colds, flu, and allergies.
- Aids in healthy liver, kidney, and gallbladder functioning.
- Supportive for type 1 and type 2 diabetes.

Dawn Chorus Tea: A mixture of nettle, green rooibos, and rose petals that can be found premixed. It was suggested that I drink one cup daily to prevent metals from being absorbed by my body. (Today, I try to include this in my routine at least a couple times a week.) I learned that metals can enter our systems not just from aluminum foil or from deodorant, but from contaminated air and water. For those who live along the Gulf of Mexico, we are affected by a dead zone located off the coast of Louisiana. A dead zone is an area of water that is unable to support aquatic life and holds onto unhealthy items such as metals.

Essiac Tea: Is a special mixture of slippery elm, burdock root, sheep sorrel, and turkey rhubarb root. It was formatted especially for use as a **cancer treatment**. It can be ordered online or in specialty stores premixed.

Green Tea: Is a rich source of EGCG, a potent antioxidant. Green tea has been found to help:
- **Cancer**
- High cholesterol
- Heart disease
- Rheumatoid arthritis
- Immune system
- High blood sugar level
- Obesity
- Infections

Note: Certain varieties of green tea and other teas may contain excessive levels of fluoride that could be harmful. Before adding tea to your diet, it's important to find a pure, organic source.

Marshmallow Herb: Since two of my health issues were skin related (breast cancer and dysplasia of the vagina) my herbalist recommended this herb. It supported me throughout my healing journey. I found it in powdered form and added it to my health drinks. The boiled root is also a great addition to healing teas.
- Heals irritated vaginal tissues, as well as those of the mouth, throat, and stomach.
- Relieves and suppresses coughing, and soothes allergies, mucus membranes, sore throat, and lungs.
- Aids inflammatory skin conditions like eczema and psoriasis.
- Overall soothing to inflamed or sore parts of the body.
- Offers antioxidant benefits - **beneficial for cancer prevention** as well.

- Prevents and fights bacteria and parasites - has antimicrobial properties.
- Aids in healing diarrhea.

Note: Take with caution if you are diabetic or have blood sugar issues.

Parasite Remedy: This tincture is a combination of black walnut green hull, wormwood, and clove. A tincture is a potent extract of one or more herbs that is aged in an alcohol base. Parasite remedy tinctures can be purchased already mixed, or as individual herbal tinctures. For ease of use, and to make sure I had the right proportion of each herb, I chose a pre-mixed remedy.

Peppermint Tea: This was not a staple of my diet, but an occasional tea for either medicinal purposes or just a change in pace.
- Relieves disorders of the gastrointestinal tract, diarrhea, and stomach cramps - promotes digestion.
- Relieves insomnia and tension.
- Relieves headaches and enhances brain and nerve functioning.

Tincture of Licorice, Pokeroot, and Eleutherococcus: This was custom prepared by the holistic medical clinic to help me heal from parasites and **cancer**, along with assisting my detoxing protocols.

Licorice:
- Healing to the gastrointestinal tract, treats ulcers, lowers acid levels, acts as mild laxative, and relieves gas.
- A powerful antiviral, antioxidant, antifungal, and expectorant, that contains phytochemicals.
- Treats upper respiratory ailments including coughs, hoarseness, sore throat, and bronchitis.
- Anti-inflammatory - relieves rheumatism and arthritis.
- Treats prostate enlargement and yeast infections; provides weight control.
- The root extract can minimize symptoms of menopause and menstruation, including cramps.
- May delay the progression of HIV to AIDS and is helpful in treating hepatitis
- Heals external and internal skin diseases, promotes healthy skin, and functions as a diuretic.
- Supports adrenal gland function and combats stress and chronic fatigue syndrome.
- Enhances healthy cholesterol levels and regulates low blood sugar.

Note: There are some side effects for licorice, including that it is not recommended for use over long periods. Research is recommended before use.

Pokeroot:
- **Good for dissolving tumors and fighting cancer cells, especially of the breast and uterus.**
- **Supports overall breast health.**
- Supports healthy lymph glands and is a lymphatic decongestant.
- Prevents and kills parasites.
- Treats skin diseases.
- Balances the metabolism, and supports immune functioning.
- Antiviral and anti-inflammatory properties, good for eye infections and respiratory problems.

Eleutherococcus (Siberian Ginseng):
- Strengthens the immune system.
- **Combats radiation side effects and exposure to toxic chemicals.**
- Reduces stress, adrenal burnout, and exhaustion, while enhancing overall energy.

Red Clover Stillingia: This herbal extract combines nine different herbs: licorice root, red clover leaf, stillingia root, prickly ash bark, oregon grape root, burdock seed, wild indigo root, buckthorn bark, and pokeroot.

- Blood purifier, working primarily through the lymphatic, glandular, and mucous membrane systems.
- Enhances waste elimination and improves nutrient absorption.
- **Often used as a treatment for cancer.**
- Aids skin diseases.
- Improves constipation, arthritis, and middle ear infections.

Slippery Elm: It is available in several forms including as tea and pills. I initially added it to my routine to help with diarrhea and intestinal issues caused by parasites. I still take a slippery elm pill nearly everyday to maintain a healthy stomach.
- Great herb for the stomach: neutralizes stomach acids, relieves ulcer and inflammatory bowel, soothes intestinal irritation, treats gastrointestinal disorders, aids digestion, cleanses the colon, treats diarrhea, and relieves the pain of irritable bowel or Crohn's disease.
- Has emollient, expectorant, diuretic, and demulcent (soothes mucous membranes) properties.
- Beneficial for chest conditions including coughing and soothing a sore throat.
- **It is a key ingredient in Essiac tea, which is used to heal cancer** and is antioxidant rich.
- Heals diseases of the female organs.
- Enhances adrenal gland and kidney functioning.

White Tea:
- Studies show the antibacterial and antifungal benefits of white tea are greater than green tea.
- Supports immune system functioning.
- **Prevents cancer**; lowers blood pressure and cholesterol, supports healthy skin, and disables yeast cells.

Note: Certain varieties of tea may contain excessive levels of fluoride that could be harmful. Before adding tea to your diet, it is important to find a pure, organic source.

Natural Vitamin & Mineral Sources

Are you looking for foods that contain the primary vitamins and minerals? Many foods have trace, or small quantities of a variety of nutrients, but the list below only includes foods with high levels of the given nutrient. This is not meant to be an all-inclusive list, but these are the best sources for these nutrients from foods that are part of my diet.

Vitamins:

Vitamin A (animal sources): Egg Yokes, Fish Oil

Vitamin A (beta-carotene sources): Seaweed (Nori), Mustard Greens, Brussels Sprouts, Spinach, Broccoli, Kale, Lettuce, Carrots, Sweet Potatoes, Yams, Winter Squash, Apricots, Cherries

B Complex: Fish, Whole Grains, Eggs, Nuts, Yogurt, Leafy Greens, Beans
Note: individual B vitamins can be sourced from individual foods.

Bioflavonoid: Lemons, Apricots, Cherries, Berries, Broccoli

Vitamin C: Broccoli, Brussels Sprouts, Cauliflower, Cabbage, Sauerkraut, Leafy Greens, Winter Squash, Mustard Greens, Blueberries, Bean sprouts

Vitamin D: Is easily obtained from exposure to the sun. Most agree that 10-15 minutes a day in sunshine, without sunscreen, provides adequate vitamin D. Your location, the time of year, and cloud cover can alter that rule of thumb. There are limited food sources for obtaining naturally occurring vitamin D, like eggs and salmon. To make sure I get my daily intake, I take a vitamin D supplement.

Vitamin E: Almonds, Egg Yokes, Leafy Greens, the Oil Component of Seeds, Nuts, and Grains

Vitamin K: Dark Leafy Greens, Yogurt, Egg Yokes, Fish Liver Oil

Minerals:

Calcium: Broccoli, Bok Choy, Collards, Kale, Mustard Greens, Spinach, Chard, Grains, Beans
Since the daily requirement is high, I always supplement with a bone booster complex.

Chromium: Eggs, Apples, Spinach, Grains

Iron: Egg Yokes, Salmon, Grains, Almonds, Brazil Nuts, Broccoli, Dried Apricots, Raisins, Leafy Green Vegetables - especially Spinach and Kale

Magnesium: Dark Green Vegetables, Nuts, Seeds, Legumes, Grains, Avocados, Apricots

Manganese: Nuts, Grains, Egg Yokes, Legumes, Leafy Greens - especially Spinach

Phosphorus: Fish, Eggs, Grains, most Fruits and Vegetables offer support

Potassium: Leafy Green Vegetables, Broccoli, Apples, Avocados, Raisins, Dried Apricots, Seeds, Nuts, Fish

Selenium: Fish, Grains, Nuts, Garlic, Onions, Broccoli, Radishes, Swiss Chard

Zinc: Egg Yokes, Grains, Beans, Ginger Root, Nuts - especially Brazil Nuts, Pumpkin Seeds

I am a big proponent of finding natural sources for vitamins and minerals, but I also feel that supplements are critical. If you know that you may not be getting your requirement in certain areas, supplementation becomes key. Make sure your supplements are varieties that can be easily absorbed and digested by your body. See 'The Key to Supplement Absorption' page 71.

Healing Foods by Health Category

This section includes my favorite foods, herbs, and supplements, but is not a comprehensive list of everything that is available to us. In other words, we know that milk is a good source for calcium, but since milk was not a part of my diet, it is not included in the list below.

More detailed explanations of each item are included in the 'Healing Foods' section, page 53. I have grouped foods by general health categories for ease of use. I always encourage you to do your own research before embarking on a new diet. It is important to seek expert advice, especially if you have a serious illness, are on prescription medication, or are pregnant or nursing.

Adrenal Glands

Garlic	Legumes	Onion
Grains	Licorice	Siberian Ginseng
Greens	Nuts / Seeds	Slippery Elm

Anti-Aging (See also Cellular Integrity)

Acai Berry	Ginger	Royal Jelly
Avocado	Goji Berry	Salmon
Basil	Grains	Umeboshi
Blueberry	Kombucha	Walnuts
Cherry	Miso	Water
Cruciferous Vegetables	Olive Oil	Yam
Flaxseed Oil	Oregano	
Garlic	Radish	

Antibacterial, Antifungal, Antibiotic Properties

All Spice	Garlic	Sauerkraut
Apple	Honey	Scallion
Basil	Lemon	Seaweed
Bay Leaf	Licorice	Tempeh
Blueberry	Lime	Thyme
Burdock Root	Marshmallow	Turmeric
Cabbage	Onion	White Tea
Calendula	Oregano	Wine
Cilantro	Oregon Grape Root	Yogurt
Cinnamon	Pokeroot	
Cranberry	Rosemary	

Anti-inflammatory, Good for Arthritis, Rheumatoid Arthritis

Acai Berry	Fish	Pokeroot
All Spice	Flax Seed	Pumpkin Seeds
Apple	Goji Berry	Red Clover Stillingia
Basil	Ginger	Rosemary
Bay Leaf	Green Tea	Royal Jelly
Beets	Lemon	Sesame Seeds / Oil
Borage Oil	Licorice	Turmeric
Calendula	Lime	Turnip Greens
Cherry	Marshmallow	Winter Squash
Cilantro	Mustard Greens	Yam/Sweet Potato
Cinnamon	Onion	Walnuts
Cranberry	Oregon Grape Root	
Eggs	Pear	

Antioxidant Support

Acai Berry	Broccoli	Onion (Red)
Apple	Cherry	Olive Oil
Apricot	Cilantro	Oregano
Arugula	Collard Greens	Pear
Artichoke	Goji	Quinoa
Avocado	Green Tea	Raisin
Barley	Honey	Rosemary
Basil	Kale	Seaweed
Beans	Licorice	Sesame Seeds / Oil
Beets	Marshmallow	Slippery Elm
Blueberry	Miso	Spinach
Brazil Nuts	Mustard Greens	Tamari

Thyme	Walnuts	Yam / Sweet Potato
Turmeric	Wine	
Turnip (Root & Greens)	Winter Squash	

Note: The best apples for antioxidants are Red Delicious, Granny Smith and Fuji varieties. Some of the best beans are kidney and black.

Blood Sugar Regulation, Diabetes

Acai Berry – Beneficial to Diabetes	Cinnamon – Blood Sugar Regulation
Almonds – Blood Sugar Regulation	Dandelion - Beneficial to Types 1 & 2 Diabetes
Allspice – Blood Sugar Regulation	Green Tea – Lowers Blood Sugar Levels
Apple – Stabilizes Blood Sugar	Hummus – Blood Sugar Regulation
Barley – Beneficial to Types 1 & 2 Diabetes	Licorice – Raises Blood Sugar Levels
Beans / Lentils – Controls Insulin, Blood Sugar	Millet – Beneficial to Type 2 Diabetes
Blue Green Algae – Stabilizes Blood Sugar	Onion – Blood Sugar Regulation
Brown Rice – Blood Sugar Regulation	Radish – Beneficial to Types 1 & 2 Diabetes
Carrots – Blood Sugar Regulation	Walnuts – Blood Sugar Regulation
Cherry – Prevents Diabetes	Winter Squash – Blood Sugar Regulation
Cilantro – Blood Sugar Regulation	Yam/Sweet Potato – Blood Sugar Regulation

Brain, Cognitive Functioning, Memory

Acai Berry	Collard Greens	Spinach
Beets	Eggs	Thyme
Blueberry	Fish, especially Salmon	Turmeric
Borage Oil	Goji Berry	Turnip Greens
Cherry	Mustard Greens	Walnuts
Chrysanthemum	Peppermint	
Cinnamon	Rosemary	

Cancer Prevention & Healing

Acai Berry	Eggs	Raisin
Almonds	Essiac Tea	Red Clover Stillingia
Apple	Fish	Romaine
Apricot	Flax Seed	Rosemary
Artichoke	Garlic	Royal Jelly
Arugula	Ginger	Sauerkraut
Avocado	Goji Berry	Scallion
Basil	Grains	Seaweed
Beans / Lentils	Green Tea	Sesame Seed / Oil
Beets	Kale	Slippery Elm
Blueberry	Lemon	Spinach
Borage Oil	Lime	Tamari
Brazil Nuts	Marshmallow	Tempeh
Broccoli	Miso	Thyme
Brussels Sprouts	Mustard Greens	Turmeric
Cabbage	Olive Oil	Turnip (Root & Greens)
Carrot	Onion	Walnuts
Cauliflower	Oregano	Wine
Cherry	Pear	Winter Squash
Chrysanthemum	Pokeroot	White Tea
Cinnamon	Pumpkin Seeds	Yam / Sweet Potato
Collard Greens	Radish	Yogurt

Cell Integrity (See also Omega-3 Sources)

Basil	Flax Seed	Thyme
Cauliflower	Kombucha	Sweet Potato

Detoxing, Cleansing

Acai Berry	Dawn Chorus Tea	Radish
Artichoke	Garlic	Red Clover Stillingia
Arugula	Goji Berry	Red Root
Blue Green Algae	Kale	Scallion
Broccoli	Kombucha	Seaweed
Burdock Root	Lemon	Siberian Ginseng
Chrysanthemum	Licorice	Turmeric
Cilantro	Lime	Turnip (Root & Greens)
Collard Greens	Mustard Greens	Umeboshi
Dandelion	Onion	

Enhanced Energy (See also Metabolism)

Acai Berry	Kale	Royal Jelly
Blue Green Algae	Kombucha	Seaweed
Dandelion	Miso	Shou Wu Chih
Goji Berry	Radish	Siberian Ginseng
Honey	Raisin	Umeboshi

Eyes

Acai Berry	Cherry	Oregon Grape Root
Almonds	Chrysanthemum	Raisin
Apricot	Dandelion	Shou Wu Chi
Avocado	Eggs	Spinach
Broccoli	Fish, especially Salmon	Sweet Potato
Blueberry	Goji Berry	Turnip Greens
Carrot	Kale	Winter Squash
Cabbage	Mustard Greens	

Fiber Sources

Acai	Carrot	Radish
Almonds	Cauliflower	Raisin
Apple	Flax Seeds	Romaine
Apricot	Grains	Sesame Seeds
Artichoke	Green beans	Seaweed
Avocado	Hummus	Spinach
Beans / Lentils	Kale	Sweet Potato
Beets	Millet	Tempeh
Blueberry	Mustard Greens	Turnip / Turnip Greens
Broccoli	Onions	Winter Squash
Brussels Sprouts	Quinoa	

Healthy Hair & Nails

Beans	Kombucha	Radish
Eggs	Nuts	Sesame Seeds
Brown Rice	Pumpkin Seeds	Seaweed

Hair Only

Apricot	Raisin	Winter Squash
Carrot	Sweet Potato	Walnuts

Healthy Nervous System (See also Omega-3 Sources)

Borage Oil	Honey	Radish
Chrysanthemum	Kale	Sauerkraut
Eggs	Peppermint	Scallion
Flax Seeds	Pumpkin Seeds	Sesame Seeds / Oil

Cardiovascular Health

Blood Pressure

Apple	Calendula	Pear
Artichoke	Chrysanthemum	Romaine
Avocado	Garlic	Sesame Seeds / Oil
Beans / Lentils	Goji Berry	Walnuts
Beets	Fish	Winter Squash
Borage Oil	Millet	White Tea
Broccoli	Olive Oil	Yam / Sweet Potato
Brown Rice	Onion	Yogurt

Circulation, Vein Problems

Acai Berry	Calendula	Ginger
Almonds	Cherry	Miso
Artichoke	Eggs	Pumpkin
Basil	Fish	Rosemary
Borage Oil	Garlic	Scallion

Thins Blood / Prevents Clotting

Eggs	Ginger	Scallion
Fish	Olive Oil	Seaweed
Garlic	Onion	

Lowers / Regulates Cholesterol

Acai Berry	Cilantro	Pumpkin Seeds
Almonds	Cinnamon	Romaine
Apple	Collard Greens	Scallion
Artichoke	Fish	Seaweed
Avocado	Garlic	Spinach
Barley	Ginger	Tempeh
Basil	Goji Berry	Turmeric
Beans / Lentils	Green Tea	Turnip Greens
Beets	Hummus	Walnuts
Blueberry	Licorice	White Tea
Borage Oil	Millet	Wine
Broccoli	Olive Oil	Yogurt
Brown Rice	Onion	
Carrot	Pear	

Protects Against Heart Disease, Regulates the Cardiovascular System, Overall Heart Health

Acai Berry	Apricot	Avocado
Apple	Artichoke	Beans / Lentils

Beets	Flax Seeds / Oil	Rosemary
Borage Oil	Green Tea	Scallion
Brazil Nuts	Hummus	Sesame Seed / Oil
Broccoli	Miso	Seaweed
Carrot	Mustard Greens	Spinach
Cauliflower	Olive Oil	Tempeh
Cherry	Onion	Thyme
Cinnamon	Quinoa	Walnuts
Collard Greens	Raisin	Wine
Eggs	Red Root	Winter Squash
Fish	Romaine Lettuce	Yams / Sweet Potato

Gastrointestinal Health

Because 80% of the immune system lives in the gut, your intestinal health is a top priority for preventing illness and disease, maintaining health, and healing most health issues. My diet was rich in foods to support my intestinal health. In general, a diet rich in fiber is always good for overall stomach and intestinal health.

Overall Good for the Stomach/Gastrointestinal Tract

Apple	Komboucha	Peppermint Tea
Apple Cider Vinegar	Lemon	Quinoa
Blueberry	Licorice	Slippery Elm
Brown Rice	Lime	Tempeh
Burdock	Millet	Turnip Greens
Carrot	Miso	Umeboshi
Ginger	Pear	Winter Squash

Aids Digestion

Acai Berry	Ginger	Rosemary
Allspice	Komboucha	Sauerkraut
Apricot	Lemon	Slippery Elm
Artichoke	Lime	Tamari
Avocado	Miso	Tempeh
Bay Leaf	Oregon Grape Root	Turmeric
Burdock Root	Peppermint Tea	Umeboshi
Brazil Nuts	Radish	
Calendula	Romaine	

Colon Health, Bowel Functioning

Apple	Calendula	Pear
Barley	Carrot	Raisin
Beans / Lentils	Cauliflower	Romaine Lettuce
Beets	Cinnamon	Slippery Elm
Blueberry	Collards	Spinach
Broccoli	Ginger	Tempeh
Brussels Sprouts	Miso	Turnip Greens
Burdock Root	Onion	Winter Squash
Cabbage	Olive Oil	Yogurt

Good Bacteria for Stomach

Komboucha	Sauerkraut	Tempeh
Miso	Tamari	Yogurt

Prevents, Treats Constipation

Apple	Carrot	Pumpkin Seeds
Barley	Cinnamon	Radish
Beans / Lentils	Licorice	Raisin
Blueberry	Oregon Grape Root	Slippery Elm
Burdock Root	Pear	

Prevents, Treats Diarrhea

Apple	Ginger	Red Clover Stillingia
Allspice	Honey	Slippery Elm
Blueberry (especially dried)	Marshmallow	Yogurt
Brown rice	Oregon Grape Root	
Cinnamon	Peppermint	

Immune Health (See also Antioxidants**)**

Acai Berry	Fish	Pear
Apricot	Garlic	Pokeroot
Blueberry	Goji Berry	Quinoa
Blue Green Algae	Green Tea	Rosemary
Brazil Nuts	Honey	Sauerkraut
Broccoli	Kale	Seaweed
Cabbage	Komboucha	Siberian Ginseng
Cauliflower	Miso	Turmeric
Collard Greens	Oregano	White Tea
Eggs	Oregon Grape Root	Yogurt

Kidney, Bladder, Urinary Tract (See also Antioxidants & Detoxing**)**

Apple	Cranberry	Radish
Artichoke	Dandelion	Sesame Seeds / Oil
Beets	Fish	Shou Wu Chih
Blueberry	Licorice	Slippery Elm
Brown Rice	Pear	Thyme
Burdock Root	Pumpkin Seeds	

Liver

Artichoke	Komboucha	Sesame Seeds / Oil
Broccoli	Mustard Greens	Shou Wu Chih
Burdock Root	Oregon Grape Root	Turmeric
Calendula	Radish	Walnuts
Chrysanthemum	Red Root	
Dandelion	Rosemary	

Lungs, Asthma, Bronchial, Respiratory Problems

Apricot	Lemon	Radish
Carrot	Licorice	Red Root
Collard Greens	Lime	Rosemary
Dandelion	Marshmallow	Shou Wu Chih
Fish	Millet	Turnip Greens
Flax Seeds	Mustard Greens	Thyme
Garlic	Onion	Turmeric
Honey	Oregano	Winter Squash
Kale	Pokeroot	

Metabolism

Brazil Nuts	Komboucha	Turmeric
Ginger	Pokeroot	Walnuts
Goji Berry	Seaweed	

Migraines Headaches, Overall Pain Relief

Allspice	Ginger	Sesame Seed / Oil
Calendula	Millet	Slippery Elm
California Poppy	Miso	Turmeric
Cherry	Oregon Grape Root	Umeboshi
Fish	Quinoa	

Omega-3 Sources

Beans / Lentils	Flax seeds	Winter squash
Borage Oil	Hummus	Walnuts
Brazil Nuts	Salmon	
Eggs - if organic omega-3 rich	Sesame Seeds / Oil	

Osteoporosis, Bone Health

Almonds	Eggs	Salmon
Beans	Kale	Seaweed
Beets	Miso	Sesame Seeds / Oil
Blueberry	Mustard Greens	Shou Wu Chih
Brazil Nuts	Pear	Spinach
Broccoli	Pumpkin Seeds	Tempeh
Brown Rice	Quinoa	Turnip Greens
Cinnamon	Raisin	Yogurt
Collard Greens	Romaine	

Parasites

Combo Tincture of: Black Walnut Green Hull, Wormwood, Clove

Pokeroot	Pumpkin Seeds

Prostate Health

Avocado	Kale	Sauerkraut
Beans / Lentils	Kelp (Seaweed)	Spinach
Broccoli	Licorice	Tempeh
Garlic	Miso	Turmeric
Green Tea	Pumpkin Seeds	Winter Squash

Note: Although not part of my diet the herb Saw Palmetto and Tomato are natural supporters of prostate health.

Skin Health

Acai Berry	Dandelion	Red Clover Stillingia
Artichoke	Eggs	Rosemary
Apricot	Flax Seeds / Oil	Salmon
Avocado	Licorice	Sesame Seeds / Oil
Borage Oil	Marshmallow	Spinach
Broccoli	Miso	Turmeric
Brown Rice	Oregon Grape Root	Turnip Greens
Calendula	Pokeroot	Water
Carrot	Radish	Winter Squash

Sleep Aid

Blueberry	Goji	Peppermint Tea
California Poppy	Honey	Walnuts
Cherry	Hummus	

Weight Loss (See also Metabolism)

Apple	Green Tea	Romaine
Apricot	Kombucha	Turmeric
Avocado	Licorice	Walnuts
Blueberry	Radish	Yam

How to Cook Your Healing Foods!

How to prepare & cook your healing foods – a few suggestions from Alice's routine.

When I share my eating and cooking routine, I get comments like, "That is so much work," or "I've never cooked *that* before. I wouldn't know where to start." I want to share a few suggestions to help get you started.

The best advice I can give is to have fun experimenting with flavors and textures. Some of my favorite recipes started as a spontaneous idea or from pairing unlikely foods together.

Streamlining the Process

I know that cooking all of your meals is time consuming and can feel overwhelming. Here are a few ideas to streamline the process:

Do your major cooking two or three times a week, not every day! I take the time twice a week to cook enough food for about three days. I know that some foods can lose nutritional value over time, but if it is lightly cooked and eaten within a couple of days, most of the nutrients will remain intact. In addition, you can incorporate freshly prepared foods with the pre-cooked foods.

While I am cooking, I like to have my laptop on the kitchen island or make brief calls, so I can be productive.

I generally cook ahead a bowl of grains (like millet and quinoa), a bowl of lightly cooked vegetables (like broccoli, carrots, and onions) and maybe tempeh or fish that can be used for approximately four meals (two meals for two days). I then fill in with freshly cooked foods like greens each day.

Cleansing Your Vegetables

This is an easy and healthy method for cleaning your vegetables and fruits. One of the owners at my local health food store shared this simple method, and I am happy to share it with you. Keep a large pot or bowl next to the sink and fill it with water. The secret ingredient is four to six drops of grapefruit seed extract. This extract has antibacterial and antimicrobial properties, which help cleanse whatever you place in the water. As you prepare your meals drop fruit, vegetables, lettuce, and greens into the bowl and swirl them in the water. This cleans the food with minimal water usage and without store-bought cleaners that may have questionable ingredients.

The Cooking Basics

Grains: Millet, Quinoa, Brown Rice, & Barley

Grains are flexible as a side dish and can be flavored to become a great accompaniment to any meal. Most have directions on the package for you to follow. If organic varieties are not available in stores near you, they can be purchased on the internet. I always add a pinch of sea salt and generally add a bay leaf during cooking for additional flavor. Bay leafs themselves are not edible, so I pull them out once the grain is cooked. Fresh herbs are always a nice addition, depending on personal taste preferences. When I can, I generally cook two grains and add them together for more texture, taste, and nutrients.

Meal ideas with cooked grains:
- Use them warm with yogurt and blueberries for breakfast. Almonds, seeds, or raisins are other wonderful additions.
- Sauté them with oil and seeds for a filling side dish for lunch or dinner.
- Stir-fry them with eggs and vegetables – a great quick meal.

Vegetables

When lightly steaming or boiling vegetables I like to add a pinch of sea salt. The water that remains after the cooking process is great to cook with, use as a base for soups, or just to sip. Drinking the cooking water helps to capture any nutrients that were lost during the cooking process. Spinach 'broth' is my favorite, followed by broccoli. Try sipping the cooking water from brown rice to help settle an upset stomach or to maintain your stomach's health.

My Mom always saved the vegetable juice when I was growing up. My siblings and I fought over who would get to drink the spinach juice. This was something that my Mom learned from her Mom.

Vegetable Variations

I always lightly boil, steam, or sauté my vegetables. After a while, I started to yearn for some taste variation. Even though I like the natural taste of vegetables, I felt like I was eating the same thing, over and over. Here are a few suggestions that I follow to add variety to my meals.
- I make use of flavorful fresh herbs. I choose herbs that have healing properties that are beneficial for my body and me.
- I sauté fresh garlic in olive oil, sesame oil, or a mixture of the two. Then I toss the cooked vegetables in the oil – yummy! Sometimes I sprinkle sesame seeds on top. This actually takes very little time to do. If the vegetables are already cooked, I can sauté the garlic and warm the vegetables in a few minutes.
- I squeeze fresh lemon juice on veggies like greens, spinach, and broccoli. It really amplifies the flavor.
- Ginger is wonderful to cook with because it adds great dimension to foods and is easy to work with. I add ginger to steamed, sautéed, and boiled foods. It can be used much in the same way as garlic.

Special Vegetable Tips

- Spinach is a quick cooking fresh vegetable. It only takes a couple minutes for it to lightly steam. Eat it on its own, with leftover grains and vegetables, or cook it with eggs.
- Most people say that greens (turnip, kale, collards, etc) need to be deeply cooked, because they are bitter. I find that steaming them for about five minutes, then sautéing them with onion and garlic is delicious, and not bitter. Not only is the cooking time shorter, but more nutrients stay in the greens. Just steaming them for five minutes with a bay leaf or with a splash of lemon at the end is tasty too.
- An easy way to cook winter squash (like acorn or butternut) is to cut it in half, scoop out the seeds, and lay it flesh side down in a pan with a little water. Cook it on the stovetop with the lid on. Bring it to a boil and then simmer until soft, approximately 25 minutes. Alternatively, bring it to a rolling boil, cover,

and turn off the stove. The steam heat will cook the squash through and I have the freedom of walking away from stove.

- Cooked squash can be scooped out of the shell and eaten alone, mashed for an interesting side dish, or pureed for use in a delicious soup. Cinnamon and allspice are great partners to winter squash, lending a slightly sweet taste.

Making a Whole Meal with a Winter Squash

Cook the squash until it is tender. At the same time, sauté oil, diced onions, almonds/walnuts, and a diced apple (I prefer tart green) in a separate pan. When the onions turn golden, add in wild caught pre-cooked salmon. (It can be found in pouches or tinned in the fish section of the grocery store.) Tear into small pieces and toss just until it is heated. Then take the cooked squash and fill it with the sautéed ingredients. It is a complete and filling meal. On the other hand, adding cooked greens or a small romaine salad on the side creates a wonderful dinner presentation. I prepare this when I have friends over, and it always gets great reviews. Stuffed winter squash without the salmon is a filling and sweet side dish too.

Quick Approaches for More than Veggies:

- Cook enough brown rice (or other grain) pasta for three meals. Pasta and vegetables tossed in oil makes a wonderful one pan meal.
- Experiment! Brown rice pasta, brussels sprouts, and spinach sautéed in a garlic sesame oil/olive oil combination is one of my favorites. Lavishly cover it in sesame seeds for a great texture experience.
- Try brown rice pasta tossed with garlic, olive oil, and sautéed green beans and leeks.

Quick Approaches that Include Protein

- Sprinkle pumpkin seeds or chopped nuts on grains and vegetables to add protein to any meal.
- A stir-fried rice or grain with one or two eggs only takes a few minutes to do if the grains are precooked.
- When legumes and lentils are eaten with grains like millet, quinoa, or barley they become a whole protein.
- Lightly cooked brussels sprouts with rice or grains make a whole protein.

Fishy Ideas

When I buy fresh caught fish, I buy more than what I need for one meal – maybe enough for three or four. I cook it all so it is quick to eat for lunch and dinner the following days.

I find it easier to cook nearly everything on the stovetop since I don't have to wait for the oven to heat up. Living in Florida, the last thing that I want during the summer is the ambient heat from the oven in the house. So, I generally brown my fish on each side using the stove. Tamari soy sauce, lemon juice, garlic, ginger, and onions are always great partners when sautéing fish.

Then add a little water or broth to the pan and cover with a lid. This keeps the fish moist and tasty. While steaming, sometimes I:

- Add slices of lemon and fresh herbs.
- Add fresh ginger and the juice of the ginger with sesame seeds.
- Add finely chopped almonds or seeds.
- Add a handful of fresh spinach to the top during the last few minutes so it steams too.
- Cover the fish with bok choy leaves for the last minute or two of steaming.
- Use a combination of these or whatever else sounds good. Be creative with your healthy foods!

Eggy Ideas

I learned that eggs have more benefits if they have a soft yoke, versus scrambled or over hard. This was a challenge for me, since I do not eat bread or wheat. How was I going to scoop up the yoke? I came up with something that is easy and tastes good. I put my over easy or sunny side up egg on top of warm grains and they absorb the yoke. It makes a great breakfast. Sometimes, I do this for a quick lunch or dinner, adding in vegetables.

Cooked Fruits
Everyone wants something that tastes sweet once in a while. A poached apple or pear is a quick and simple way to fill that craving. Poaching the fruit keeps it from drying out, which sometimes happens to baked fruit.

How do you poach fruit? Cut the apple or pear in half and place it flesh down in a small amount of water in a lidded pan on your stovetop. I like to add allspice and cinnamon to the cooking water. Bring it to a boil, and either simmer for a few minutes until soft, or turn off the heat to steam cook it. Great warm by itself or with chopped nuts and raisins. It tastes like a sweet dessert, but no sugar is added!

Salads
I have found that olive oil, lemon juice, and a little sea salt make a healthy, delicious salad dressing. Here are some great additions to salads for both variety and a healthy protein source. Be daring in your salad combinations.
- Add black beans, pumpkin seeds, and scallions. For an extra zing, use seeds roasted with spices.
- Try avocado slices (remember it has some protein in it) either alone or with scallions and seeds.
- Add crumbled wild caught cooked salmon.
- Add a scoop of hummus.
- Add almonds or walnuts.
- Add warm brussels sprouts to the top of your salad.
- Add a generous scoop of quinoa.

Beyond the Basics

How to Use Fermented Foods
Many organic fermented foods are expensive, but they have many health benefits. Here are some ideas about how to get those benefits while being cost conscious.
- Umeboshi Plum Paste: Best used as a condiment, placed on the side of a plate. Because of its strong taste, I only use one teaspoon with a meal.
- Sauerkraut: Another great condiment. A serving is a heaping tablespoon. I also like to add it to my tempeh towards the end of cooking.
- Miso: A soup base and a flavorful broth for cooking. See the 'Recipe' section, page 89, for more ideas.
- Tamari: Great to flavor with and can be used like soy sauce. I use it while cooking tempeh and fish.
- Tempeh: I sauté it with onions, tamari, vegetables, and miso for a main dish. See the 'Recipe' section, page 89, for more ideas. (This is an inexpensive, alternative protein source.)
- Komboucha: I consume one to two bottles a week, because I only drink 1/4 of the 12oz bottle, each day.

Fermented Food Ideas for Intestinal Health:
When you have an upset stomach or intestinal virus, fermented foods will help settle your stomach and return it to a normal pH level. Here are three that I used most often when my stomach needed support.
- Make a cup of miso and sip it.
- Take a cup of warm water and add a teaspoon of umeboshi, several drops of fresh squeezed ginger root, and 1/2 teaspoon of tamari. Stir and sip. Thanks to my sister for sharing!
- Sip komboucha more frequently.

Fresh Ginger Root Tips:

A friend of mine shared a great idea for keeping ginger root fresh. If you have worked with this root before, you know that it can become dried and withered quickly. If we are spending the money for organic foods, we want to be able to use what we purchase.

To prolong ginger's shelf life peel the skin off the root and then cut the flesh into small pieces, the approximate size that you would use for cooking. Lay these pieces on a flat surface in the freezer, so they are not touching each other, just until frozen. Then place them in a freezer bag and store in the freezer. Freezing the ginger before storing keeps the pieces from becoming stuck to each other, so you can easily access the amount you need for cooking.

Also, try using a garlic press to squeeze ginger root juice from a small piece. I love to do this over a piece of salmon while cooking. The ginger flavor really becomes integrated into the flakes of the fish.

How to Use Seaweed:

A large portion of seaweed isn't necessary to get the health benefits. Some varieties of seaweed have a strong taste that may take time to become accustomed to eating. However, if you add a small amount a few times a week, your body will thank you.

- Most nori is packaged and sold in sheets. It has a mild taste and is the type of seaweed that is used for sushi rolls. Take 1/8-1/4 of a sheet and tear into small flakes to use with rice, grains, and soups.
- Wakame is a traditional ingredient for miso soup. Take one dehydrated strip or a few small pieces, depending on what you buy, and place it in a bowl of water for about five minutes to re-hydrate it. Cut up as needed. You can also add re-hydrated wakamae to rice, vegetables, and blended raw drinks.

Raw Foods:

In addition to nuts, seeds, an occasional raw apple, pear, and recently plum, I have a salad approximately five times a week and a blended raw vegetable drink almost every day. These were not part of my original macrobiotic diet. However, I find that in moderation, they are agreeable to my body and I get the benefits from raw vegetables. I also enjoy the taste of raw vegetables and their crunch.

Blended Raw Vegetable Drinks

I suggest including greens like collards, kale, swiss chard, romaine, etc, in blended raw vegetable drinks and to rotate the kind of greens that you use to get the best health benefits. I like to add a little lemon, lime juice, or fresh ginger to the drink. For a spicier drink, try adding a little turmeric, which has great health benefits. I usually include turmeric in my drinks and it pairs well with lemon, lime, and ginger. Sometimes, I like a lighter blended drink with carrots, spinach, cilantro, and a touch of lime or lemon juice.

Raw drinks, along with soups, are a great way to use up vegetables before they have a chance to spoil.

Recipes

Hummus

Hummus is a healthy creamy dish that is most often used as a dip. Until recently it was hard to find organic hummus, and when I did, it was quite expensive. The good news is that hummus is easy to make. Canned organic chickpeas, also called garbanzo beans, and dry organic chickpeas can be found in many stores. Using canned beans is obviously quicker, but always remember to rinse them. If you decide to cook the dried beans yourself, soak them overnight and change the water before cooking. Cooking time should be approximately two hours or until tender.

Try combining chickpeas with other beans such as northern or white for a smoother hummus. Experiment with adding different vegetables in the puree for a one of a kind hummus creation.

It is best to blend 1/3 to 1/2 of the recipe at a time, so your blender/processor can best do its job. Slowly add a few tablespoons of water to get the consistency that you desire.

A common ingredient in hummus is tahini, which is sesame seed paste. It is found in the ethnic section of the grocery store and is used primarily in Middle Eastern cooking. Although it is not necessary to use tahini to make hummus, it does lend a unique flavor to the dip.

Try organic crackers, organic corn chips, brown rice crackers with hummus. Raw or slightly cooked vegetables like carrots or broccoli also taste good with this bean dip. Hummus can be served at room temperature, cold, or even warm. It keeps well in an airtight container for several days in the refrigerator.

Because hummus is a good source of protein, I like to add a scoop on the top of my salad or eat it with my grains and vegetables.

For the most part, it is one of my preferred snack foods. If you are snacking in the evening, it actually can help relax you for a good night's sleep – it is one of its healing properties. Enjoy the many health benefits of the ingredients in hummus.

Traditional Hummus

Ingredients

1 can chickpeas or 1 cup dry chickpeas	Juice of 1 lemon
1 tablespoon tahini	Sea salt, to taste
1 garlic clove	3 tablespoons extra-virgin olive oil

Note: For those who are limiting their oil intake, it is not necessary to add the olive oil. However, most hummus recipes will call for some amount of oil.

Directions

Fully rinse canned chickpeas. If dry chickpeas are used, soak overnight and cook until tender on low to medium heat, rinsing when done. Place all ingredients except the extra-virgin olive oil in a food processor. As the ingredients blend, add a small amount of water and olive oil gradually until desired consistency is reached.

Hummus with a Middle Eastern Topping

Ingredients

1 can chickpeas or 1 cup dry chickpeas

2 garlic cloves

Juice of 1 lemon

3 tablespoons extra-virgin olive oil, plus more for drizzling

3 tablespoons tahini

Sea salt

Turmeric

Directions

Fully rinse canned chickpeas. If dry chickpeas are used, soak overnight and cook until tender on low to medium heat, rinsing when done. Combine chickpeas, garlic, lemon juice, extra-virgin olive oil, and tahini in a food processor and blend until ingredients come together into a thick paste. With the food processor running, add a little water, about a tablespoon at a time, until the hummus becomes smooth and creamy. Add sea salt to taste. Transfer the creamy hummus into a bowl and dust with turmeric. Drizzle with extra-virgin olive oil before serving. In addition, I sometimes like to add spiced roasted pumpkin seeds to the top.

Roasted Pumpkin Seeds

Ingredients

Pumpkin seeds

Olive oil

Sea salt

Possible spices: cayenne pepper, thyme, pepper, tamari, garlic, turmeric, cajun spice, and chili powder

Directions

Preheat the oven to 300 degrees F. Toss the pumpkin seeds with oil and dust with sea salt and desired spices. Place on a cookie sheet and roast for about 30 minutes - turning occasionally. Alternatively, place the pumpkin seeds on the cookie sheet first and then add the oil and spices on top.

Note: I do not usually advocate eating spicy foods, but every once in a while it is fun to have a change, especially if it is with something as healthy as pumpkin seeds.

Quinoa Salad

A friend shared this recipe with me.

Ingredients

1/2 cup dry quinoa

1/2 cup water

1/2 cup apple juice

1/4 teaspoon cinnamon

1/8 teaspoon ground cloves

1 red apple, cored and chopped

2 teaspoons lemon juice

1/2 cup raisins

1 cup chopped celery

Directions

In a medium covered saucepan bring the water, apple juice and spices to a boil. Then add the quinoa. Return to a boil, cover, and cook over low heat for 15 minutes. Let cool, then add the apple and toss with the lemon juice, raisins, and celery. Makes 4 servings

Quick Miso Soup

Ingredients

Carrot, chopped	Pinch sea salt
Onion, chopped	Miso paste
Water	Scallions
Several dried wakame flakes per serving	Lemon

(The amount of ingredients that you use depends on how much miso soup you want to prepare. Sometimes I am in the mood for the plain miso soup without any vegetables, while other times I want a few, or even lots of vegetables. The soup allows you to be flexible, and I often use whatever I happen to have on hand.)

Directions

Soak dried wakame seaweed for 5 minutes in water – chop if needed. Place the carrots and onion with water in a pan, simmering until vegetables are slightly cooked - approximately 5-7 minutes. Add the wakame, and the water it was soaking in, to the vegetables. Bring back to a slow simmer. Add miso paste to the soup and stir until dissolved. The standard ratio is 1-2 tablespoons of miso per cup of liquid. Garnish with sliced scallions and/or a small amount of lemon juice.

Other vegetables can be added instead of, or in addition to, the carrot and onion. Leek, cabbage, and celery are some of my favorites. Alternatively, just plain broth with wakame, scallions, and lemon is delicious too.

If you do not have vegetables or wakame on hand, just heating the miso paste with water is warming and satisfying.

This entire process takes less than 10 minutes. Miso paste keeps in the refrigerator and has a long shelf life. It is easy to prepare one cup at a time for a quick pick me up or when your stomach feels upset. Without vegetables, it takes just a few minutes to prepare.

Because it is light broth, it is a great starter for your meals. Guests are always impressed when I serve miso soup as the first course.

Millet

Ingredients

1 cup of dry millet	Pinch of sea salt
2+ cups of water	A few tablespoons of olive or sesame seed oil

Directions

In a skillet, lightly brown 1 cup of millet in a few tablespoons of oil. Then add 2+ cups of warm water and simmer for about 25 minutes. (Most recipes call for boiling millet. I find that it is very flavorful to brown it before boiling.)

Eat warm with a couple tablespoons of organic yogurt and some blueberries for breakfast. Seeds and nuts are great additions too. Use the grain for lunch or dinner with vegetables and a protein source. The grains can be refrigerated and warmed up as needed.

Tempeh

Tempeh is found in your local health food store or in the refrigerated section with either organic or tofu products in the grocery store. It is a nutty tasting, alternative protein source.

Ingredients

1 package of tempeh
Tamari soy sauce
Onion or leek, diced

1/2 - 1 cup of water
1-2 tablespoons of miso
Olive or sesame oil

Optional: carrot, cabbage, sauerkraut, herbs such as thyme, oregano, bay leaf, and caraway seeds

Directions

Preheat oil in a lidded skillet. Cut tempeh into bite size squares and add to the pan. Sprinkle tamari on the tops of the tempeh squares. Sauté for 5+ minutes, turning once to brown each side. Add onion and continue to sauté for another 2+ minutes. Add water. Add miso paste, stirring to dissolve. (This can also be done separately in warm water, to make sure that it fully dissolves.) Add the desired vegetables and herbs. Cover and simmer over low heat for 20+ minutes. Serve over healthy grains.

Serve with sauerkraut on the side, sprinkle with seeds, or even serve with mustard. Alternatively, adding sauerkraut in the pan towards the end creates a wonderful dish. I love to add sauerkraut juice, the flavored water that the kraut is stored in, instead of miso, when I have it.

Squash / Carrot / Sweet Potato Soup

I use this recipe, or variations of it, with carrot, squash, or a combination of the two. A sweet potato is another great addition to this soup. Basically, any orange vegetable you have on hand will work well in this soup. A wonderful substitute for the ginger is curry. It is a delicious hot soup, but is also surprisingly tasty when served cold.

Ingredients

2+ tablespoons olive oil
3.5 cups chopped carrot, squash, or both
1 large onion, diced (I prefer Vidalia if available)
1 green apple, cored, peeled, and chopped

3 cups vegetable broth
Pinch of Sea salt; season to taste
2 teaspoons fresh minced ginger
Plain yogurt and carrot curls to garnish

Directions

Sauté the onion in oil until it is soft. Then add the apple and ginger, with enough water to cook. Simmer until the apple is soft and set aside. In a separate pan, cook the orange vegetables in water until soft. Place in the blender/food processor with enough of the cooking water to make a smooth mixture. Add back into the pan. Blend the apple/onion mixture and a little water until smooth. Add to the carrot/squash mixture and stir. Add additional vegetable stock as needed. Bring to boil, and adjust seasoning to taste. Serve each bowl with a swirl of yogurt and a few curls of raw carrot.

This recipe lasts for several days in the refrigerator. It is tasty, but also very warm and soothing to the stomach.

Other Soups:

Sometimes the vegetables that I buy start to go bad, before I get a chance to cook them. Using them in a soup is a way to use up what I have on hand. Here are a few of my experimentations.

A barley vegetable soup is always tasty and easy to prepare. Pureed soups create a nice even flavor and have a great texture. I have experimented with a pureed artichoke/leek soup, broccoli/leek soup, and leek/spinach/kale soup. On the last one, I added some of the puree (before it was diluted to soup consistency) to my hummus. Great change!

One fun experiment was with a leek, kale, chickpea, and carrot soup. I sautéed sliced leeks and minced garlic in olive oil with turmeric. Separately I boiled the cut up carrots. I blended a small amount of green leek leaves and kale, 1/3 of a can of rinsed garbanzo beans, some minced garlic, and fresh oregano leaves. After blending, I diluted with water to make the broth for the soup.

I then added the remainder of the can of rinsed garbanzo beans, the sautéed leek mixture, and a few chopped kale leaves to the carrots and their cooking water. I stirred in the pureed diluted vegetable mixture and seasoned with cayenne pepper, sea salt, and turmeric to taste. After bringing all of this to boil, I served it with a squeeze of lemon.

This was just creatively put together from what was in my refrigerator and pantry and it turned out great. So get creative with your soups.

Lentil & Brown Rice Dosas

My assistant shared this recipe with me and I really like it. It is a great alternative source of protein and includes a brief fermentation process. You do have to prep it 1.5 days ahead, but it is so easy to do. You can also refrigerate unused batter, or leftover dosas.

Ingredients
1/4 cup lentils (red lentils are suggested, but any will work)
3/4 cup brown rice (long brown rice suggested, but any rice will work)

1 cup water	Cayenne pepper
Oil	Salt
Turmeric	Pepper

Directions
Put lentils and rice in a container with the water and soak for 8 hours. Then, blend in a blender or food processor and let the mixture sit for 24 hours. Do not refrigerate! Add spices. I chose to add turmeric, cayenne pepper, salt, and a little black pepper. Heat a skillet with a little olive oil. Dosas will cook much more evenly if the pan and oil is hot before the batter is added. Spoon three tablespoons of batter and spread to a 6" diameter. Lightly brown both sides like a pancake. The flatter the dosas are the better they will cook.

They can be eaten as is, or with various dipping sauces like peanut, tamari with ginger, yogurt, or umeboshi. Dosas can be eaten with a nice salad and vegetables for a full meal, or use it as an alternative to wheat sandwich wraps. You can make them as spicy or as mild as you want. I am not a big salt eater, but this seemed to need a decent amount of sea salt. It surprisingly rises to make quite a bit from only 1 cup. I used leftover dosas the next day for breakfast by heating them up and laying an over-easy egg on top.

One Final Note

If you cannot manage cooking healthy organic foods everyday, I recommend that you start by doing so a few times a week. Even baby steps, are still steps forward.

After I found the rhythm for this type of routine, it was easier to do because it became my routine. I have found that when I go off my cooking and eating regime, my body does not like it. My colon especially kicks up a storm.

I just feel better when I eat healthy, exercise, get fresh air, rest, meditate, and think positive thoughts. It's all a matter of finding balance.

The Importance of Sleep

Why Sleep was in My Top Three Priorities

We all push ourselves to keep up. There are always things that need to be done, and we put an enormous focus on making money to support our families and ourselves.

When faced with a major health issue, it is critically important to honor and support your body's healing with lots of rest and lots of sleep. That means taking one to three naps a day, plus sleeping longer than usual at night. Why? Your body best heals when it sleeps. Your body has the ability to rebound and heal, if you allow it to do so.

I was challenged in this area. I work for myself and financially support myself. When I do not work, there is no money coming in to live on. However, my body was telling me that it wanted to lie down and take a nap.

When I honored my body by taking naps during the day and sleeping longer at night, the next day I would feel so much better. I would then end up doing more that day, too much more. This was my Achilles heal, because I would fall back two steps the next day and feel exhausted again.

I learned quickly that getting lots of sleep was one of my top three priorities that must be done each day, despite what my 'have to's' were.

When my intestinal problems started draining me, I had no choice. I had to sleep. I cut back on my workload from 100% to 25%. I turned my situation over to God, asking for the financial means to pay my bills. I had no choice but to totally surrender and trust. I simply had no energy and had lost a great deal of weight during this period.

I finally allowed myself to rest as needed to restore my body's health. I allowed myself to say, "It will be okay somehow." When those two things happened, my body started to respond faster to the healing tools that I was embracing.

I have my assistant to thank for this breakthrough as she observed the cycle of falling back, over and over. She suggested doing less each day, despite how I felt. This meant even if I had the energy, I should still lie down and take a nap. This fueled the process for a quicker recovery.

Even if you are not sick, sleep is still important. It is one of the most important things you can do for your body's health. It is more restorative than all of the products on the market today, and it is free. Organizing your life so you get the highest quality sleep possible is well worth the effort.

Why Sleep is Important for Health & Healing

During deep sleep, growth hormone production is at its peak. This growth hormone speeds up the absorption of nutrients and amino acids in your cells, aiding in the healing of tissues throughout your body. It also stimulates bone marrow, and because this is where white blood cells are created, it is critical to your immune system's proper functioning.

The hormone melatonin is also produced during sleep. This hormone inhibits tumors from growing, prevents viral infections, stimulates your immune system, increases antibodies in saliva, has antioxidant properties, and enhances the quality of sleep.

Studies have shown that when sleep is deprived, the natural killer cells necessary to ward off disease dramatically decrease. We want those cells healthy to keep us healthy!

I received in a meditation that it was important to set an intention for my night's sleep. Specifically, I asked my guides and angels to help heal my body and to make sure that my energy did not drain away while I slept. This made my sleeping process even more productive.

Taking time to rest & allow the universal energy of love to take over & heal.
7/23/0?
Alice

If you are having problems sleeping, try placing an amethyst next to your bed. This crystal calms the mind and nervous system, soothing you into sleep. As you place the stone next to your bed set the intention that it will help you to sleep fully and deeply each night.

Also, refer to the 'Establish a Healthy Home & Site Environment' section, page 118, for other insights into what can negatively affect your sleep and what you can do about it.

Most importantly, if you are healing, rest. It is okay. If you are not sick, but your body is tired, honor it and go to bed early. Listen to what your body is telling you.

Other Places that Support Healing

Sleep and rest are a must for healing. There are, however, other places that inspire healing or a healing experience. Most are found outside in nature. Whether you are able to enjoy these locations in real time, in visualizations, or in meditations, I hope you enjoy them as I do.

Some of my favorite places for inspiration and healing are:
- **The Beach**. The rhythm of the waves lapping on the beach, the fresh air, and the warm sunshine helps to lull you inside of yourself, to that special place where healing occurs.
- **The Lake**. The stillness of the water and its ability to reflect what you need to know provides calmness and insights that support healing.

- **The Mountains**. There is nothing like being on a mountaintop to bring forth the feeling of being connected to God and all that is. This feeling of connection and alignment fosters total trust in your healing, as well as inspiration and insights.
- **The Woods.** It is calming and renewing to be in the center of God's vegetation. The consistent canopy of trees offer shade and protection from the sun, and provide a cool respite to travel inside of yourself
- **Waterfalls or a Water Garden**. The sound of running water is cleansing. Close your eyes and allow the running water to cleanse and heal you inside and out.
- **A Private Garden**. Intimate and protected, your private garden is a great place for meditation and journaling. Both activities support healing and its manifestation within your body.

Alternative Medical Support

Acupuncture

I was introduced to acupuncture around 1990. This was before I received the healing gift that I have now. I had a car accident in December of 1989, which left me in extreme pain on the right hand side of my body. I couldn't even hold onto a toothbrush or spoon without extreme pain.

I tried everything, but nothing helped. Only acupuncture, selected Chinese herbs in pill format, and deep tissue massages had an impact. Over time, the pain lessened to the point where I almost felt normal. Intermittently over the next 10 years, the pain on the right side of my neck, shoulder blade, and arm would come and go. Although I could live with it, it never really went away and could be very painful at times. It was not until I did my first total energetic spiritual healing on myself in 2001 that it left and never returned.

What I learned was how important it is to find and heal the root cause of the problem to prevent it from returning. I also learned that acupuncture is a wonderful practice that assists your body to heal naturally.

If you combine transformational healing and acupuncture, you have a winning game plan. Add the right diet, nutrition, and some of the other protocols I have in this book; then, you are surely set for success.

From this first experience in 1990 to the present, I have always used and recommended acupuncture to support the healing process. That is why I chose acupuncture to support my body's ability to heal breast cancer.

However, not all acupuncturists are equal – just like not all dentists or doctors are equal. I chose the acupuncture physician that I did because unlike others in my area, she:
- Did needle insertion herself versus delegating it to someone else.
- Used meditation for intuition and guidance. She did not limit herself only to textbook formulas.
- Naturally emanated a bedside manner that was calm and healing, yet confident.
- Had a degree in Chinese medicine (acupuncture) and in Chinese Herbology.

I have learned that there are people who practice acupuncture, but don't have a four-year degree. I prefer those that went through the full four year degree program, and I believe you should too, as they have a better understanding of how to work with the energy meridians in your body.

When you find someone good, go to him or her even if it is not convenient. I drove an hour for my appointments, because it was worth it.

What is Acupuncture?

Acupuncture is a 5,000 year old Chinese medical practice. It works with natural vital energy to promote the body's ability to heal itself. It is based on an energetic model. Energy flows along specific meridians, or pathways. Each pathway is associated with a physiological system or internal organ. Ill health represents an imbalance that hinders the needed energy flow along your pathways. Needles are used to release or add back energy, balancing your entire body's system. It is a systemic approach to supporting your body's health and healing. I always leave my acupuncture sessions feeling relaxed and restored.

Bringing Acupuncture into Your Daily Life

A complete map of your body exists on your ear lobes, feet, and hands. In other words, there are pressure points corresponding to every part of your body on your feet, hands, and ear lobes. You can support your body's healing by putting pressure on the points that correspond to your health issue.

My acupuncture doctor used the practice of affixing small seeds on certain areas of my ears to effect change. This provided a subtle ongoing pressure in between acupuncture sessions. If I wanted more support, I would put more pressure on the seed with my fingers – lightly squeezing it for a few moments. This created a renewed energy flow in the corresponding area of my body, in the same fashion as an acupuncture needle.

Learn the acupuncture touch points on your feet, hands, and body, or keep a good diagram nearby. It is especially helpful to know the points that relate to what you are working on healing. You can support your body simply by placing pressure on the associated points when you need extra pain relief or just to accelerate your body's healing. Adding essential oils to certain locations heightens the experience.

My acupuncture physician also recommended a few protocols that support tumor reduction: herbal pills like *Mammo-Guard* and *Immune II*, along with *Oumei Breast* patch and topical cream.

Chiropractic

Although I did not engage in chiropractic treatment for my diagnosis of cancer, I wanted to include it in this book as I use chiropractic treatments when needed. Throughout my life chiropractic care has given me the relief and healing support that my body craves. There were a couple times during my journey that I felt my body was out of alignment, and I used chiropractic adjustments to address it. Misalignment can hinder your body's overall health. Why?

The spine houses your spinal cord, and with the help of your brain, they are your central nervous system responsible for sending nerve messages throughout your body. In fact, each spinal vertebra has a nerve connection to certain parts of the body, feeding them information through nerve signals and impulses.

Spinal misalignment can occur from physical traumas, emotional issues, or even birth experiences. This misalignment can lead to nerve interference, diminishing the normal supply of impulses and proper nerve functioning. When this happens, pain and ill health are fostered in the areas of your body that are connected to the misaligned part your spine. Chiropractic adjustments bring your spine back into alignment, restoring nerve functioning, and allowing healing to occur.

If you do not feel comfortable with acupuncture, the chiropractic modality is a good alternative. Both approaches work with your body to systemically, support health and healing.

Medical Diagnostics

The Gift of Diagnostics

About six weeks into my journey, I had terrible diarrhea that left me weak and dehydrated. It would not end and I lost 16 pounds very quickly. How could I heal if I could not absorb my food? In fact, it came out in undigested clumps. I had tried taking Chinese teas, but as soon as I drank them, I had to run to the bathroom. I tried to respect the process as cleansing, but soon I knew it was way too much. I took myself off the teas, which helped a little, but didn't change the big picture.

I was dehydrated, had little energy, was too thin, and was scared. The diarrhea would not stop, but my journey continued to lead me to the right solutions. I learned about a Medical Intuitive in my area. I went to her to get advice on what supplements I could eliminate. The amount of pills I was taking was a little overwhelming and hard to digest, especially in this situation. She suggested that I was weak and needed the intervention of an IV of silver. She told me about a holistic medical clinic. Its focus is to heal from the inside out and is staffed with medical doctors, naturopathic doctors, a physicist, and supporting holistic practitioners.

Although I was diagnosed with cancer, I was going there because of my severe intestinal problem. At this point in my journey, I had already effected the change in my tumor from the inside, but had no 'medical proof'. My bigger issue was that all of my nutrition was leaving my body as soon as it was ingested.

I decided to travel six hours and spent one week at the holistic medical clinic. I received the gift of intervention: Large IV doses of silver, vitamin C, and multiple vitamins/minerals. It really bolstered me as the needed nutrients were absorbed directly into my blood stream, bypassing my digestive track.

The bigger gift, in the long run, was their diagnostics. The clinic conducted diagnostics - thorough work-ups of saliva, bowel, urine, blood, skin (scratch test), and gastro. They analyze this information looking for the areas that you are deficient in and recommend supplements to address it. This supports your body to heal naturally. Although I was there for the digestive issue, they reviewed the supplements I was taking for the cancer diagnosis, and they fine-tuned about 15% of my regimen.

While I was there, the gastro test and the scratch test came back. The gastro showed dysfunction in my small intestine, which is where 80-90% of your nutrients are absorbed. This made sense! This was why I was so weak, thin, and dehydrated. We added supplements such as enzymes, a tincture of cinnamon, and other herbal extracts that are good for the stomach. However, we did not know why this was happening.

Several weeks later, I received a call from the clinic. Although only some of the results were in, I was told that they had uncovered parasites. This information, as well as the results from the other tests, was very helpful in addressing what I was deficient in and what was needed to bolster the overall health of my body through adjusting my supplements and foods. It also guided my transformational energy work to focus on parasites.

Not all areas of the country have good alternative care. I had to drive over six hours one-way to utilize this clinic. You are worth it. Spend the time to travel to those who can help you.

For more information on foods to help you when you are dealing with intestinal problems, including diarrhea see 'Healing Foods by Health Category', page 81.

Parasites

When I was told the news about the parasites, I was in disbelief. How did I get those? People feel like they can only get parasites in undeveloped countries. We can get them here, from a variety of sources and even from eating raw foods. Some suggest that we all have small amounts of parasites, fungus, bad bacteria, and cancer in us, believing that when our stomach becomes out of balance these things can take over and multiply. Once again, your intestinal health is critical. When they 'set up house' within your body they can be very difficult to get rid of. This held true for me.

Additionally, there is a link between having parasites or fungus and developing cancer. Many feel these are the cause of most types of cancer. While I do not think they cause cancer, I do think they certainly can make it easier for cancer to grow and are draining for your immune system's limited resources.

When I learned that I had parasites, I immediately:
- Asked for support from colleagues.
- Focused on healing my body energetically. Now that I knew what it was, I could address it.
- Researched what approach to use to support my body's release of these unwanted invaders - holistic versus traditional medicine.

I was already focusing my diet primarily around healing and soothing foods for my stomach. I did not know what was causing my intestinal problems until late September 2007. Once the parasites were discovered, I could target my spiritual, energy healing work on the physical cause of my intestinal issues. As soon as I learned I had parasites, I did a strong round of energetic healing. Three things stand out from this work.

One: A friend and colleague of mine did an amazing Reiki session on me focused on expelling the parasites. When I got home that night, I had to go to the toilet and it was like gas explosions – fireworks.

Two: I was invited to do a healing circle for the Earth with a group of woman, and it became a healing on each other. I asked for help with the parasites. That night I had the same experience.

Three: I did an incredible piece of work, supported by a fellow healer. I explain that experience in detail earlier in this book on page 14. I am completely grateful for that wonderful experience. Immediately when I came out of the deep work, my stomach felt calm. I finally had relief from the constant and severe cramps. They were gone!

I took the time to research what remedy to use for my body. Should it be a prescription medicine or a natural remedy? I learned that any medicine that a doctor would want to prescribe could force the parasites further into the intestinal wall. So, I chose a natural remedy, a tincture containing fresh green hull from black walnuts, wormwood, and clove. Initially, the tincture made my stomach cramp again, but that soon stopped.

I also used pumpkin seeds in a specific routine first thing in the morning. One handful of seeds was chewed all at once and swallowed. I repeated this three times. Then I waited about 20-30 minutes before drinking a glass of water. Often a laxative or a food that offers a laxative effect is ingested a few hours later to clear the bowels. Pumpkin seeds were already in my diet, but not in a concentrated manner. This method helps immobilize and expel the parasites from the intestinal walls. When I researched pumpkin seeds, one of the many healthy attributes included helping to expel parasites.

Towards the end of my parasite healing, I purchased a zapper that is worn on your wrists. It omits a frequency that apparently helps kill the parasites and their eggs. Although I did not wear it as frequently and for as long as recommended, I did use it, as I wanted the extra assurance.

There are different types of zappers, but generally, they are a low voltage device that supposedly kills parasites, bacteria, and viruses with electrical energy, but does not harm human tissue. They are based on the idea that all living things emit radio frequencies and that the device can issue counter-frequencies that kill unwanted organisms.

My symptoms of intestinal distress came on strong in late July 2007. I learned I had parasites in September 2007. Although I felt vastly improved in early December, I did not have proof of my healing until I received another round of diagnostic reports in February 2008. However, it was not over yet. I had to retrain my gastrointestinal tract to produce needed digestive enzymes by using tools like supplementation and energy healing. Some healthy foods, like greens, are hard to digest. It took almost a year for me to be able to properly digest them.

I found the entire episode to be more painful, draining, and longer than my experience with breast cancer. The herbal tinctures tasted nasty, my stomach was constantly distressed and bloated, and diarrhea was my constant companion. I am determined never to have this experience again, so I have incorporated three simple prevention steps into my routine. I prepare my own raw foods at home, seldom eating raw foods in restaurants. I continue eating foods that are primarily alkaline with lots of fiber. I support my intestinal health with fermented foods and a daily probiotic supplement, both of which contain 'good' bacteria. I suggest that you do the same.

Cleansing & Detoxification

I knew it was important to cleanse and detox my body of the mental and emotional toxins, as well as the environmental toxins that we breathe and ingest. Although I had undergone several herbal cleanses in the past 10 years, I never did anything stronger or deeper. I knew this would be critical to my healing, and I always advise my clients to embrace some type of cleansing routine.

Diet & Supplements

For my healing journey with breast cancer, my choice of macrobiotic diet was naturally cleansing. I ate foods that are cleansing such as turmeric, blue green algae, and miso soup. My herbal teas contained properties that helped cleanse and support my liver, kidneys, and spleen, which is important during detoxification. A supplement called *Drainage Quest* assisted in clearing congestion and impurities in my lymphatic system. Vibrational protocols did their job by shifting and cleansing all parts of me.

During my metal detoxification journey in 2008, I continued the detox regimen that I created with several new additions. My acupuncture physician suggested two teas, chrysanthemum that is good at detoxing metals and dandelion for cleansing by increasing urine. Dandelion also replaces potassium that is lost in urine, boosting energy levels. In the terms of Chinese medicine, dandelion helps improve chi or vital energy. I was grateful for this improvement because I was very tired. It is common to feel depleted, tired, or dehydrated when going through a detoxification. I also used Shou Wu Chih, a Chinese tonic, to replenish and nourish my liver and kidneys, along with enhancing my energy. I needed extra support as my body had been detoxing over a long period, as this ended up being a six month journey. The holistic clinic recommended herbs, chelation supplements, and stepped up the usage of *Drainage Quest*. I also added cilantro to my blended health drinks. Cilantro acts as a natural chelation agent and therefore is great for metal detoxification.

For both detoxification experiences, I made sure that my supplements and energy work supported my liver, kidneys, and spleen. These organs were the most taxed during this process.

Protocols

Detoxification Footbaths & Saunas

I had just started to research alternative medical devices like detoxification footbaths and saunas, when I first visited the holistic medical clinic. I was excited to learn that this clinic had these as well as other equipment that could support my cleansing and healing. While there, I had a chance to learn about and use portable footbaths that help detoxify the body, along with a portable sauna that utilizes both ozone oxygen and infrared heat.

Infrared heat penetrates deep into the body, helping expand the peripheral blood vessels. This increases circulation in the soft tissues and muscle tissues, as well as delivering oxygen-rich blood to your body, speeding the natural recovery process. It also is a great aid for detoxification and toxin elimination.

Ozone, which is a potent form of oxygen, stimulates the immune system, cleans arteries and veins, improves circulation, purifies the blood and lymphatic system, normalizes hormone and enzyme production, reduces inflammation, oxidizes toxins allowing their excretion, and chelates heavy metals. A recent discovery is that our own neutrophils, a type of white blood cells, actually manufacture ozone.

Our exposure to toxins has dramatically increased in recent years, and they can be reduced through ozone and infrared heat. This makes the in-home capability of these saunas a great tool for illness prevention, maintaining well-being, and healing. There are saunas available that are only offer ozone therapy or infrared heat, but I feel that by combining both I have a total package for good health.

I was quite fortunate that the clinic was able to work with me so I could make payments without interest for one year. This allowed me to purchase both the sauna and the footbath, so I could incorporate them into my weekly routine at home. During most of my healing journey, I did footbaths and the sauna three times a week. I also received an infrared heat lamp that helped breakup the tumor, and whatever else was inside of me, making it easier to release it. I still use the sauna and footbath periodically to maintain my health and I am proud to share them with clients.

Colon Hydrotherapy

I used colon hydrotherapy at the holistic medical clinic, and was able to find a local resource for colon hydrotherapy too. I used my local resource to support me at the end of the parasite ordeal and at the end of the metal detoxification process.

What is colon hydrotherapy? It is a gentle infusion of warm water through the colon. It effectively washes away old toxic waste accumulated along the walls of the colon. This cleanses trapped impurities, which prevents the recycling of toxins into your blood stream. A single colonic treatment is said to be equivalent to several enemas. Colon hydrotherapy is usually administered or assisted by a trained professional.

I now do colon hydrotherapy every 12-18 months for maintenance. If you do colon hydrotherapy, please take extra probiotics to reestablish your good bacteria, because this process clears out all bacteria - bad, as well as good.

It is important to do something to cleanse your body. It is a critical part of the healing process. Periodic cleansing or detoxification is also a good practice to prevent disease and maintain optimum health.

Practices that Center, Balance, Oxygenate, & More!

Your body consists of trillions of cells that provide the energy to carry out all of the functions, movements, and needs for your body and all of its parts. There two primary ways that your cells can source this energy – nutrients from digested food and oxygen. Both are required for optimal cell functioning. I have discussed food, so let's focus on oxygen.

Normal cells weaken, die, or mutate into unhealthy cells, if they are not properly oxygenated. For example, cancer cells derive energy through the break down of cell tissue that can occur when oxygen is lacking. Cellular oxygen starvation can contribute to immune deficiency, intestinal problems, cardiac conditions, sleep and respiratory disorders, anxiety, depression, headaches, fatigue, dizziness, and cancer. The simplest way to keep your cells from becoming oxygen deficient is to focus on long deep breaths. Breathing from your chest, causes shallow short breaths, so the goal is to breath from your belly to heighten oxygen levels. There can be other contributing factors to lacking proper cellular oxygenation like anemia, infections, parasites, and more.

My choice of a combination of yoga, Pilates, Qigong, meditation, breath work, & walking, not only provided the needed oxygenation support for my healing, but they also kept me centered, balanced, healthy, and in touch with my inner self.

Breathing Techniques

In order to heal and maintain the health of our cells, they need to be fully oxygenated. Breathing from your lower belly, like what is practiced during yoga, is very healthy. Before my healing journey, I had embraced several practices that heighten oxygen levels. However, I felt that I needed something more to really oxygenate the cells of my body and assist in holding onto a higher level of energy that would support my healing. I contacted a local yoga expert and friend who shared two specialized routines that helped fill my needs. One of them included Kundalini postures and breathing techniques.

Kundalini breath moving energy!

Alice 7/21/07

In terms of every day living, simply taking a moment to focus on a few deep breaths from the lower stomach can be calming and revitalizing. It is a great tool whenever stress or fears creep in. Combining focused breathing with visualizations, like breathing out a given fear, can enhance the experience.

Meditation

Whatever you do with full awareness is a form of meditation. Focusing only on your breath is meditation or listening to a water garden is meditation. Anything that frees your mind from distractions can be a meditative experience. In the simplest terms, meditation means 'a cessation of thought processes'. It describes a state of consciousness, when your mind becomes free of its constant thought chatter, promoting a deep state of relaxation and awareness. There are many benefits to meditation like reducing stress, increasing happiness and stability, decreasing anxiety or depression, lowering blood pressure, reducing cholesterol levels, and enhancing spiritual growth.

Going to the heart for guidance! 7/21/08 Alice

Although all of my healing work was done in a meditative state, I also included time for personal meditations to help calm and center me, as well as provide needed wisdom and guidance. I started by putting aside time for personal meditation everyday, but it slowly evolved to being about three times a week. I received so much beneficial guidance from my connection to God, my angels, and my deceased relatives in meditation. I am eternally grateful. My body and mind were also grateful for the total relaxation that meditation brings.

I want to remind you of the spiritual experiences that can occur during healing sessions. Having these experiences is so incredible, that they are wholly life changing. It is easy to start craving this type of experience beyond healing work. Why? They are so rewarding that you may just want them to be part of your ongoing life. The good news is that spiritual experiences can be attained as part of an ongoing practice of meditation, especially if you add tools like intention setting.

Qigong

The word Qigong can describe either a medicinal practice or an exercise practice. Both are rooted in a 5,000 year old Chinese healthcare modality - sometimes called 'meditation with movement'. The word Qigong is formed by the roots 'qi' (pronounced chi) meaning air, breath of life, or vital energy of the body, along with 'gong', which means self-discipline, the skill of moving, or the cultivating and balancing of qi. The exercise practice of Qigong is similar to Tai Chi, but I find the movements easier. Qigong is a system of stretches and other movements that synchronizes your breath and body, using guided visualizations. The purpose is to regulate your mind and breath to promote the flow of qi, or energy. Qigong exercises can be an excellent tool to support self-healing and inner harmony.

Although I had experienced medicinal Qigong in the past, it was not available in my area. I was aware of the exercise practice of Qigong prior to my diagnosis of breast cancer and had practiced it occasionally.

During my journey, I became much more regular about it. It made me feel good. I incorporated a 15-minute routine via a DVD that guided me, every morning. As I moved into my journey, I did this routine about four times a week. This routine facilitates the releasing of old qi and taking in new qi. It also helps to move energy in your body and balance your heart. Today I incorporate Qigong as part of my daily morning walk on the beach.

Pilates

Pilates is a form of exercise that emphasizes a balanced development of your body through core strength, flexibility, and body awareness in order to support efficient, graceful movement. Core strength goes beyond the surface muscles to utilize your deep internal muscles to maintain stability in motion. No matter how much abdominal work I used to do, it did not give me the results, or develop the core strength that I get from Pilates.

The Pilates studio that I go to has reformer beds and weight bearing resistance straps for an optimal workout. My Pilates instructor is exceptional and offered to tailor some routines to incorporate more chest opening and lymph stimulating movements, to support healing my diagnosis of breast cancer. In my Pilates workouts, we focus on breath, while strengthening and stretching muscles. This is useful in moving energy through your body and releasing toxins. The routines are challenging when you are healthy, so while I was healing I always rested extra on the days that I had Pilates workouts. I had moved my gym workouts to the Pilates studio a few years earlier, and since that time I have faithfully met my twice a week commitment to myself for this practice. Beyond staying in shape and helping to prevent osteoporosis, which runs in my family, I just feel good when I do Pilates. When I go out of town and miss my Pilates work out, I can notice the difference.

Yoga

Authentic, traditional yoga is a discipline aimed at training your consciousness for a state of perfect spiritual insight and tranquility. Today, in the Western World, yoga is commonly known as a practice of physical postures, poses, breathing, and meditation. There are many different styles of yoga, but the common goal is balancing one's mind, body, and spirit.

I did yoga once a week, primarily Flow Yoga, prior to my diagnosis of breast cancer. In addition to this practice, I discovered a DVD of Yin Yoga that I became almost addicted to. It has you hold deep poses that are not very comfortable for more than six minutes, while focusing on your breath. Most forms of yoga stimulate energy flow in the muscle tissue. This work stimulates energy flow in the deep tissue and the connective tissue, which is where my health problems were. I literally felt a detoxing and releasing effect from it. The DVD is 75 minutes long and ends with a meditation, so I could not do it everyday. However, I did this routine at least three evenings a week. It cleansed my body and relaxed me, aiding in better sleep. Besides being a good workout, all types of yoga help to clear your mind and bring focus to your breath.

Walking

Walking has many benefits and it requires no prescription, has minimal side effects, and is free. A few benefits of walking are, managing weight, reducing the risk of heart attack and stroke, controlling blood pressure, boosting good cholesterol, preventing hip fractures, reducing the risk of breast cancer and type 2 diabetes, preventing depression, lowering stress, strengthening muscles, bones, and joints, and much more.

Walking my dog in the fresh air has always been part of my daily routine. It is good for me and for her. As I progressed into my healing journey, I sometimes needed to lessen the length of our walks, depending on how I felt, but I never missed a day. Walking is always good exercise, and offers an opportunity to connect with nature and all of the universal elements. I also like to use this time to focus on my affirmations and to listen to God's voice. One of my favorite benefits of this great low impact exercise is that it helps the lymph flow freely throughout your body. This is always important to your body's health, but especially so while healing breast cancer.

Walking for at least 30 minutes a day at a moderately brisk pace, five or more days a week is usually recommended. If you need motivation to stay on track, make a walking date with a friend.

In Summary

All of the practices above help improve and support your circulation, immune system, and the oxygen levels in your cells, in addition to providing overall fitness benefits. Most offer lymph support, encouraging it to flow freely and chest or heart openings that are created through movement and proper breathing. This, by the way, also facilitates energy circulation in your breast. However, the biggest gift for me was that these practices kept me centered, focused, and balanced during my journey.

As a minimal preventative maintenance routine, take 10 minutes a day to just sit and breathe from your belly, and incorporate one or more of the other practices weekly. You will enjoy the many benefits that each practice offers. Find the one, or combination, that best resonates with you.

Maintain a Healthy Stomach & Lymphatic System

Eighty percent of the immune system lives in the gut, and sluggish lymph hinders the immune systems performance. It is critical to maintain a healthy intestinal environment and free flowing lymph liquid for all parts of you to be healthy.

Healthy Stomach

My diet was the biggest contributor to keeping a healthy stomach. I planned my food around what would help maintain or benefit my stomach's health. Organic, alkaline foods that are not yeasty and are lightly cooked are best for overall intestinal health. This means limiting or excluding all wheat, cheese, dairy, meat, sugar, caffeine, and peanuts from my diet. See 'Healing Foods by Health Category', page 81, for specific foods that support intestinal health. A few of the best foods include miso, millet, quinoa, small amounts of organic yogurt, cruciferous vegetables, carrot, winter squash, blueberry, apple, ginger, cinnamon, allspice, burdock root, oregon grape root, licorice, slippery elm, and komboucha. In addition, a strong probiotic has always been part of my daily routine.

Essentially, you control the health of your stomach by what you put into it. It is that simple.

Healthy Lymphatic System

Clear, free flowing lymph is the key to your body's health. Patterns and emotions become easily buried in our lymph nodes and glands, limiting our ability to have free flowing, joyful lymph. I worked on transforming this area for myself, using the tools of my healing practice. In addition, I added two lymph drainage supplements *Drainage Quest* and *Lymphomax*. I still take *Lymphomax* daily. Red root and pokeroot are also good herbs for keeping the lymph healthy.

The health of your lymph can help or hinder your overall health, as it is a major part of the immune system. It is also very linked to breast cancer, because your underarm lymph glands are adjacent to your breasts. Therefore, I wanted to do all I could to keep my entire lymphatic system healthy.

I learned how to do a light self-massage to stimulate my underarm and breast areas, which I did a few times a week. When I visited the holistic clinic in late August, I had a professional lymph adjustment and massage.

I also purchased a small trampoline. Jumping for at least five minutes a day kept my lymph flowing. Other exercises like Pilates and even walking support healthy lymph, but the trampoline only takes a few minutes a day to make a big impact.

Towards the end of my journey, I learned about dry brushing. If the other approaches are not appropriate for you, try dry brushing. The process actually lightly brushes your skin, with a soft natural fiber brush, in specific patterns that correspond with how your lymph flows through your body. This stimulates your lymph to circulate freely. It is important that your body be dry, to properly complete a dry brushing. It is usually suggested to shower or bathe afterwards to wash off the impurities that are released from dry brushing.

I chose to do all I could to facilitate a healthy lymphatic system with a combination of herbs, supplements, exercise, and my own energy healing work. I would like to encourage you to do your own research to find a routine that best suits you. For those who are healing, do all that you can to have healthy lymph flowing unobstructed through your body. Even if you are not currently healing, maintaining a healthy lymphatic system amplifies your immune system, helping you stay healthy now and into the future.

Support from the Healing Arts

It is always helpful to reach out for support. We are not supposed to do everything ourselves. I am blessed that I received support from several of the healing arts during my journey. Kinesiology, Reiki, massage, and medical intuitive readings were the primary healing arts that I turned to when needed. Each has benefits, along with complementing the overall healing process and the capacity to maintain health.

Kinesiology

Sometimes called body testing, kinesiology is an alternative care method that provides input from your body as to what it needs, what it is lacking, and what needs to be cleared and healed. It is an alternative form of medical diagnostics. Evaluation of normal and abnormal body functions can be accomplished by using muscle tests. A part of the body is used, like an arm, to answer yes/no questions. For instance, pressure is applied to an arm and a question is asked. How it responds to that question, either by holding strong or collapsing under the pressure, correlates to a yes or a no answer. I sought out a professional to do kinesiology, prior to receiving the results of the complete diagnostic work up in early October 2007. It helped guide some of my supplement decisions, as well as providing helpful information to direct my healing priorities. I find kinesiology to be an objective, accurate look at what your body needs.

Reiki

I value Reiki as a good support for healing and stress management. To support my healing of breast cancer, I had three individual Reiki sessions and each yielded exceptional results. I was also invited to participate in a Reiki group, which was helpful. During my metal detoxing journey, Reiki helped boost my energy levels, as the process left me feeling exhausted. Certified Reiki practitioners channel energies from a limitless source, God force, through their being to help your body heal. They can move energy and restore order to the body's vital energy when it has become unbalanced. This is usually accomplished by the laying of hands on your body. However, most practitioners are able to do Reiki healing from a distance. Reiki works best when the client is open and has a pure desire to heal. Reiki can aid in better sleep, help to relieve pain, assist the body in cleansing and healing, and support the immune system. A great side effect of Reiki is a deep feeling of relaxation. I always feel better after a Reiki session.

Massage

There are times when you feel like your body needs physical nurturing and healing. This is especially true when you are healing a major health issue. I choose to support and nurture my body by giving it a healing massage five times during my journey. A body massage not only makes you feel better, but also gives attention to the parts of your body that need it. The benefits are far reaching from improving circulation, to bringing fresh oxygen to your body's tissues. Massage assists in the elimination of waste products, and boosts the immune system. In the hands of a talented massage therapist, other modalities like reflexology and essential oils may be incorporated to create a one of a kind experience. It is always helpful to honor your body by giving it a massage.

Medical Intuitive Readings

When you are healing, there are lots of decisions to make regardless of whether you are taking a traditional or non-traditional approach. Although I used the counsel of my own heart and soul in meditation, sometimes I needed confirmation or additional input. For this, I sought the help of a Medical Intuitive. A Medical Intuitive is a psychic or intuitive counselor who specializes in perceiving information concerning the human body. They have the gift of being able to energetically read the inside of your body's organs, blood, bones, etc. This work is done by intuitively scanning the body for areas of imbalance that may need alignment or treatment. Some can see or sense what is wrong, others communicate with spirit guides, and a few are gifted to use a combination of the two. Some Medical Intuitives scan the energy of your body with their hands, picking up information when they feel something that is off. I used two people in this field, one was in person and the other was over the phone. Both were helpful with guidance regarding when I could lessen or stop using some of my supplements. One also helped me determine whether another round of metal detoxing was needed. Their input was always enlightening, especially at times when I was unsure of what direction to take.

Screening: Thermogram

Use a thermogram instead of a mammogram, which puts radiation into your body.
Radiation may cause potential cancer to grow.

The lump in my breast felt dormant about five weeks into my journey, but I could not prove it until I learned about a thermogram. I had a thermogram less than four months after the cancer diagnosis and it validated what I already knew. It showed no possible indictors of cancer in my breast. I had another scan three months later, and again it showed no indicators of cancer. I was even told that another scan was not necessary for 12 whole months! Every subsequent thermogram reports that my breasts remain normal and healthy. (See the 'Appendix', page 136.)

Most of the traditional medical community does not encourage or recommend a thermogram, but they have to honor the report as it is analyzed by specially trained medical doctors. Mammograms put radiation into your body, which adds up if you have one done every year to discern if there are any signs of cancer. That radiation may actually support the growth of cancer cells. Some people believe that we all have cancer cells in us. Why risk zapping them with radiation every year, possibly encouraging growth? In general, radiology uses radiation, and is not healthy for your body. Why continue to use it when there is a healthier alternative?

Even if cancer is detected through a mammogram, an ultra sound is still needed. The next step is a biopsy to confirm if it actually is cancer. There is potential danger during a biopsy. When the cancerous cells are removed from deep breast tissue, they have to move through unaffected, healthy tissue. The risk is that the cancer may spread to those unaffected cells, due to the biopsy.

This is a costly process: My biopsy was over $1800, the mammogram was $400, and the ultra sound was $775. This totaled close to $3000, without the doctor and office fees. My insurance did not cover this, but even with a policy that has a 20% co-pay it leaves over $600 for you to pay out of pocket. All of this was for ONE breast. Alternatively, a thermogram scans the upper part of the torso. This includes breasts, lymph, underarms, chest, front of neck, upper back, and back of neck. The cost is $180 for the first scan, and only $133 for every subsequent one. Unfortunately, this is not covered by insurance. However, it scans more areas and is less money out of pocket. Thermograms are not limited to upper torso scans. Whole body scans cost $360, but if you are targeting a certain area, for instance your legs, most thermographers will create a special package for you.

Thermograms are not available in many locations, but to me it is worth it to travel. My travel time is two hours each way. However, I made the best of it, going with a friend, having lunch, and doing a little shopping. Today, I sponsor a certified clinical thermographer to travel to my area. Approximately three times a year she conducts scans for those in my area, using my home office.

How does a thermogram work? It is actually a better early detector of cancer because it scans for heat. In the simplest terms, it is a series of images, which capture the natural heat variations of your body. The color ranges from white and red, which are the hottest; to green and blue, which are the coolest. Greens and blues are what you want your body to look like when it is scanned. Health issues like cancer or arthritis give off heat, so they would show up as white or red.

Thermograms can pickup a small speck of cancer, smaller than what mammograms are able to identify, making it better for early detection. Mine was the size of the top of my pinky finger, and yet there was no sign of it in the mammogram the year before. The doctor who performed the biopsy said this was about the standard size of early-detected cancer. To be that size means that it had been growing in my breast for some time. My first thermogram showed a surprise - my left breast was actually in cooler shades of blue than my right. Only three months earlier, a biopsy showed cancer in my left breast. I knew it was the result of the healing energy and loving attention that I had given my left breast. I am thankful for the transformation of the unhealthy tissue.

Thermograms are a non-invasive method that measures heat patterns emitted from the breast. It can identify abnormal blood flow and energy patterns, which affect the health of breast tissue. The first thermogram is considered a 'thumbprint' of the breast tissue, establishing a baseline for each subsequent scan to be compared with. If new heat patterns appear, it could signify that your body is moving to feed something that is at a conception stage. Now this is really early detection.

Besides not using radiation, this process does not compress the breast, which is painful.

My thermogram confirmed that my work had changed the inside of my breast. The lump was still there, but smaller. Without the thermogram, the only way to prove the positive change would be to re-biopsy. I didn't want to take that risk, or put my body through the painful process again. With a thermogram, you see indicators of potential cancerous cells, even if a tumor still exists.

Dr Christiane Northrup, a prominent breast cancer specialist, is a proponent of thermograms. Her newsletters are a great source of information on thermograms and alternative resources. However, not all doctors see it that way. My GYN was not happy about my approach, but I continue to send the scans and reports to her. She has resigned to accept them and add them to my medical file. I have made it clear that I will not be using a mammogram again.

Alternative Support Remedies

Alternative support remedies can help align the body with the spiritual and mental changes you are creating through spiritual and energy healing. I incorporated these modalities into my routine to speed up the healing process. All of these remedies can be utilized at home.

Herbal Remedies

Medicinal herbs and herbal teas were a big part of my healing armory, and I have talked about them throughout this book. I wanted to make sure they are acknowledged as an important alternative support remedy. All are discussed in greater detail with their health benefits in the 'Healing Foods' section, page 72.

I started working over the phone with a herbologist and healer when I found out I had level 3 dysplasia of the vagina. This was a full two months before my diagnosis of breast cancer. (Dysplasia is displaced, unhealthy cells that form a lesion. If they remain there too long, they can turn into pre-cancer.)

The herbs that were recommended included garlic greatly diluted in water and calendula petals steeped in water for douching. First, I did the garlic douche for about two weeks, and then the calendula petal douche for about three weeks.

This was supplemented by other herbs including:
- Marshmallow powder that was added to my morning health drink.
- A mix of red, burdock, and oregon grape roots steeped for a tea, which I drank two or three times a day.
- Red clover stillingia, which is an herbal extract that I took daily in a little water.
- Kelp powder that I put a pinch in my health drinks to supplement my iodine intake.

The suggested herbs and the transformational energy healing at a cellular level reduced the size of the vaginal lesion by 50% and changed the status from level 3 dysplasia to level 0. This occurred in approximately seven weeks. One year later, my annual exam of the cervix and vagina indicated that all was normal. This was altered with only two things, transformational energy healing work and medicinal herbs.

My herbologist also supported me in the early stages of my breast cancer healing with several important healing sessions. He recommended that I continue to use the same herbs to support healing the diagnosis of breast cancer.

Starting the very first week of my healing journey with breast cancer, I was doing my transformational healing at the cellular level, using herbs, acupuncture, and adjusting my diet and supplements. I consider these the most important steps to overcome any health issues.

Vibrational Protocols

Although I had medical proof that the diagnosis of cancer was no longer true on October 4th 2007, my lump was still there. It was shrinking at a moderate pace, but I wanted its complete exit as soon as possible.

In late November, I learned about vibrational protocols. They are only available in a few states in the US. I decided to try them with the prospect that they would help shift the vibration and energy of my body more quickly, reducing the lump to nothing. The vibrational protocols were a great support. I could literally feel myself rattling on the inside for the first week or so. I knew they were doing their job, helping to reduce the remaining lump.

To get the proper protocols that fit my needs, I sent a recent photo of myself along with a cotton swab of saliva to be analyzed. A detailed report and recommendations were formed from that analysis. The vibrational protocols look like water, are clear, and are tasteless. Each protocol is programmed with a vibrational frequency that targets a specific area that needs improvement.

I believe that this protocol was responsible for shaking loose the metal in my bones and tissues that ultimately made my body toxic. That might sound like a negative side effect, but this needed to happen for my long-term health and well-being. Those toxic metals had to be released, and the vibrational protocols initiated the process along with the detoxification sauna and footbath. Then I used a different set of vibrational protocols to assist me with releasing the metals.

Homeopathic Remedies

A wide variety of homeopathic remedies are available to us. Even most health food stores carry a selection of remedies. Homeopathic remedies stimulate the body's vital force into action. Using the philosophy of the "Law of Similars," a remedy that would cause problems in large doses will stimulate healing of similar problems in a small homeopathic dose. Through a process of dilution and succussion, the physical molecules of a substance nearly disappear, but an imprint of its essence provides a healing charge. It is the energy or vibrational pattern of the remedy, rather than the chemical content that stimulates healing. Homeopathic remedies are believed to work in the spiritual plane, meaning that the vibrational pattern affects your being from the spiritual level versus the physical.

I used a homeopathic remedy called arsenicum to assist with the dysplasia in my vagina. When I was experiencing extreme diarrhea, prior to knowing that the cause was parasites, I learned that the same remedy would be a good support. It made a huge difference in minimizing the severe cramping and pain in my stomach. When it was really severe, I took more homeopathic pills, which have no negative side effects, unlike many over the counter or prescription remedies.

Essential Oils

Essential oils are the essence of various plants, herbs, spices, and flowers. They hold concentrated healing properties that correlate to that specific plant. Typically, they are used topically versus internally. It is important to use oils that are 100% pure therapeutic grade. Do not use synthetic oils or oils with animal proteins. I used a combination of lavender, frankincense, and clove essential oils. I used the following proportions; approximately 8-12 drops of lavender, to 4-5 of frankincense, to 1-2 of clove. Some oils, like clove, are so warm on the skin that they need to be used sparingly to prevent a negative reaction. It is generally recommended that skin warming oils like clove be used in combination with other oils.

When I received in a meditation to love my lump to best support its healing, I began gently rubbing these oils over the affected area of my breast with love. I also used oils on the top of my feet where my three middle toes meet the foot. Using the principles of reflexology, this area of the foot corresponds to a healthy breast.

Rain Drop Therapy with Essential Oils

I had a wonderful experience with Rain Drop Therapy. This healing modality was developed by Gary Young who incorporated part of the Lakota Native American healing tradition into his therapy. The Lakota's worked during the Northern Lights with essential oils using feather strokes. He incorporated the Lakota feather like massage strokes, with essential oils and reflexology, in his Rain Drop Therapy.

The traditional Rain Drop Therapy uses seven essential oils on the feet and spine but a practitioner can use oils intuitively. For my health issues, ten essential oils were rubbed into the soles of my feet and toes, with a focus on the correlating spinal section of the foot. Oils were also dropped along my spine and felt like they were raindrops as they hit my skin. Each essential oil was layered over the previous one with light stokes to massage them into the spine. Hot compresses were added to aid absorption, so the oils could seep into the deep layers of my skin.

This therapy can help any health issue from the common cold to serious diseases. Most essential oils have antiviral and antifungal properties which, when applied to the spine and feet, are absorbed and transported throughout the body. This experience was relaxing and healing. It beautifully combines the benefits of massage with essential oils, but is also much more than the sum of its parts.

Establish a Healthy Home & Site Environment

Your health can be positively or negatively affected by the energy of your surrounding environments, and by the physical practices you use at home. This section is dedicated to the steps you can take to make sure that your surroundings fully support your well-being.

Practices to Promote a Healthy Home

Energy Maintenance

When I move into a new space, the first thing I do is an energetic space clearing. I clear it with my healing guides, angels, sage, toning, clapping, and intention. I have even had clients request that I do a space clearing for them when they don't like the energy of a space, or just moved in. Why is this important?

It is possible for energy from the previous occupants or events to remain in a home. Alternatively, in a new space the energy of those who built it may linger, long after it is completed. Even if you haven't had a recent move, periodically clearing your space is always a good idea.

Placing crystals around your home that absorb and transform negativity is one of the simplest steps to maintain healthy energy in your environment. Amethyst crystals are excellent for this purpose. I keep a very large amethyst cluster in my healing room for this very reason. If you decide to place crystals such as amethyst in your home, it is important to cleanse them periodically either by burning white sage or washing them with salt water. (For more information on crystals, see page 30.)

Many people place tobacco or salt around the perimeter of the house for protection. Using positive intentions with any of this work is just as important as the physical act of doing it. For example: "I intend that the salt that I am placing around my house protects me and my home environment."

Feng Shui

I also use the principles of Feng Shui to create a healthy, peaceful, and harmonious environment. There are so many aspects of Feng Shui that it could be a reference book in itself. If you are not familiar with the concept of Feng Shui, I encourage you to become acquainted with this ancient energy art form. For the purpose of this book, I want to highlight a few things that can directly impact your health.

If you leave your bathroom doors open and your toilet seats up, it can affect your energy levels. By Feng Shui principles, your energy literally is going down the drain! It is especially important to make sure all lids are down and bathroom doors are closed. If your home has a bathroom off of the master bedroom, make sure the door is closed when you sleep at night. You do not want your energy going down the drain every night.

The center of your home represents your health. Keeping it clean and free of clutter is a simple step to energetically ensure better health. This area also likes the color yellow, which is a color that is supportive of overall health. If yellow doesn't work for your design tastes, products of the earth, such as pottery, tiles, and stone, are great alternatives.

I always add intention setting when purposefully placing an object in my house. Placing a yellow vase in the center of my home, I would set an intention like, "This yellow vase helps keep the center of my home, happy, healthy, and full of good things. This yellow vase helps keep me happy, healthy, and full of good things."

Why are You Bringing Bacteria into Your Home?

I've had a 'shoes off' practice in my home since I moved to the beach in Northwest Florida. It is the easiest way to keep the sand out of the house. People honor it, by taking their shoes off just inside my door. This has long been the customary practice in other parts of the world, such as Asia.

During my healing journey, I discovered an even more important reason for this practice. Shoes can walk bacteria into your home.

After walking into public restrooms, city streets, yards where there are animals, and other questionable places, bacteria and filth are carried into your home on the soles of your or other's shoes. That same dirt and grime can become trapped in the fibers of your carpeting and other areas of your home.

In 1991, the EPA conducted a study that measured the amount of lead dust in homes. In homes where a doormat was at the entrance and shoes were NOT worn inside, there was about a 60% reduction of lead dust and other chemicals in the home environment. The study also noted a reduction in allergens and bacteria in the home.

Removing your shoes has been scientifically proven to reduce contaminants in the home. An added benefit is that it makes maintaining your carpets and floors much easier. It takes a little time to become accustomed to the habit of kicking off your shoes as you enter your home, but it is a simple change that makes your home environment healthier.

Electromagnetic & Geopathic Stress

The effects of electromagnetic fields that originate from power lines, mobile phones, computers, and sub-stations are increasingly becoming a hot topic. The concern is that they can negatively affect your mental, emotional, and physical health.

Electromagnetic fields are invisible to the naked eye. However, they are present in nearly all homes, offices, and factories. Studies suggest that electromagnetic stress can contribute to insomnia, lethargy, depression, allergies, headaches, learning problems, aches and pains in the joints, as well as cancer. The bottom line is no one knows the full effect that these invisible invaders may have on our health and well-being.

The Earth is magnetic in nature. The term 'geopathic stress' is used to describe the effects that electromagnetic fields can have on the Earth, air, ley lines (which run in a grid pattern across the Earth), or underground water. Geopathic stress is caused by electromagnetic frequencies and electromagnetic pollution from sources like cell (microwave) towers, broadcasting stations, power lines, and the like. This pollution is attracted to the natural ley lines of the Earth and slowly transforms them into something that is energetically toxic. Other factors like mining, underground tunnels, and train systems negatively impact the natural magnetics of the Earth as well.

All animals are sensitive to the Earth's energy. They will not rest or sleep on any spot that has unhealthy energy like geopathic stress. In fact, many, like my little dog, revel in rolling around on a spot of grass when there is good energy. They always manage to find their way back to that same spot over, and over. In times past, people would observe where the cattle would lay to rest and sleep. This became their obvious choice for a home site. In most areas, it is no longer possible to use this as an indicator. Therefore homes or buildings could be situated on unhealthy sites.

Similar to animals, our bodies are electromagnetic in nature and are very sensitive to the magnetics of the Earth. When your space on Earth has geopathic stress, it disturbs the delicate balance of your body. Think about how you feel sitting on the beach or on a mountaintop. Now consider how you feel inside an office space with lots of computers, or on a subway in a major city.

Inside the Home

It is hard to control and protect against environmental toxins and stress in the world at large. However, we do have more control in our home, if we choose to act on it.

Electronic equipment like computers, televisions, stereos, microwaves, and cellular phones are harmful to your health and well-being. When I do space clearings, the rooms that have electronic equipment always have flat vacant energy. We want our rooms to be full of vibrant energy!

There are several products on the market that help protect you from electromagnetic stress. Some are worn as a necklace, while others can be placed around the piece of electronic equipment you are trying to counteract. Like everything, there are expensive and inexpensive versions of this technology, but most seem to range from $100 and up. I chose to research natural solutions, looking for elements from the earth instead of manmade materials. My search led me to the natural crystal stone fluorite. This beautiful stone can be found in small sizes to easily place next to computers and other equipment. Fluorite protects against electromagnetic stress, actually shielding computers. It absorbs and neutralizes negative vibrations and emits stabilizing energy, bringing order to chaos. A small stone usually ranges from $5-10. As you place your fluorite set the intention that it will protect you and your home environment from electromagnetic stress.

Using fluorite, I can stay on my computer much longer than before, without feeling exhausted or experiencing a burning sensation around my eyes. That was how my body experienced the side effects of electromagnetic stress.

Here are some other simple steps you can take to combat electromagnetic stress:
Do not sleep with the television on. Besides the electromagnet stress coming off of it all night long, think about what your subconscious is hearing all night. You may be absorbing negative words, emotions, and energies, that otherwise would not be a part of you.

Cell phones also emit electromagnetic stress. One of the side effects for me is an unusually hot cheek, where I hold the phone against my face. Although many feel that the emission is at a low level, more and more people are finding it very helpful to use devices that can be placed on your cell phone to neutralize the harmful frequencies.

When you hold a laptop computer on your legs, do you feel the heat and uncomfortable energy that penetrates your body? A friend of mine suggested putting my laptop on a tray, like the style that is used for eating in bed. This creates a space and puts a material barrier between the harmful energy and your body.

I am not an expert on this topic, but you need to be aware of the possible harmful effects from all electronics, including the convenient microwave oven. There is conflicting evidence as to whether there are health risks to using a microwave. However, just consider these simple findings.

The same deformation that occurs in our bodies when you are directly exposed to radar or microwaves also occurs in the molecules of foods cooked in a microwave oven. This radiation results in the destruction and deformation of food molecules. Microwaving also creates new compounds, which are unknown fusions not found in nature. Studies have shown that the actual composition of your blood changes, and not for the good, when eating microwaved food.

So, it is probable that your food is broken down, not giving you the same amount of nutrients it otherwise would, and unwanted and unhealthy molecules are formed, which you ingest. In addition, you are putting unwanted, harmful microwaves of energy into your home environment.

Whether the findings are conclusive or not, I have chosen not to use the microwave. I have opted for cooking nearly all of my food on the stovetop. You might also want to consider alternatives like convection ovens, which cook food faster, at a lower temperature, and with better results than a conventional radiant heat oven. They also do not have the potential health risks of a microwave oven.

Site Dowsing & Clearing

Around the time that I was experiencing intense diarrhea, I was continually feeling exhausted. My sister who is an intuitive Feng Shui consultant wanted to dowse my property to see if there were any underground waterways present. I readily agreed to having my property dowsed and if necessary, cleared. Geopathic stress, which can be toxic to humans, is held in deep underground water veins or in grid lines that run through the planet. This is similar to the principles of meridians that circulate energy in your body that is prevalent in Chinese medicine. If your meridians become blocked or drained, your vital signs weaken and your immune system can become compromised. The same is true for the Earth's meridians, and their condition can affect your well-being.

Our body's time for repair and renewal is at night when we sleep. If your bed is positioned above an area of concentrated geopathic stress, your health can be dramatically affected. This dynamic literally drains your energy, contributing to illness and exhaustion.

When a dowsing is done properly, it connects one to the level where everything is known, and one becomes aware of the energy impulses in that space. The swinging pendulum or dowsing rods act like conductors, tuning into frequencies that are beyond what our five senses can detect.

Her dowsing found that the area where I resided had been thrown into stress due to several hurricanes. This caused the life force of the area to be drained and created a fearful energy. Specifically, under my property she found two wide branching water veins crossing beneath my bed, creating a channel for highly charged negative energy. I finally realized why, after moving into this home, I would wake up feeling exhausted, despite a long and deep night's sleep.

She intuitively received a diagram of what the energy looked like, including grid lines that were tightly constricted, which she drew for me. She used her team of spiritual guides to energetically reroute the waterways, so they did not run under my home. The rerouting was carefully done so it did not negatively affect any of my neighbors.

She then received and drew a second map that showed no remaining grid lines and only one positively charged water vein far from my bedroom.

After this work, I began waking up feeling rested. It also had a positive effect on my body's ability to catch up with the healing that I was engaging in, both spiritually and mentally.

For me, this experience reaffirmed that the advice I receive in my meditations is always helpful, even if I do not understand why in that moment. A month earlier in meditation, I was guided to ask my soul family to surround me while I slept, so my energy would stay with me. I did this even though I didn't understand why. Now I understood why that advice was given.

The dowsing work was done from a distance. She lives in New Jersey, and I live in Florida. If you are exhausted or sick all the time, you might want to have your area dowsed to see if there are unseen contributors to your problem.

Other Suggestions

This section includes pertinent information regarding bras, metals and aluminum foil, and plastic.

Bras

I was shown in a meditation how to adjust my bra around my chest and how to lower the straps for a looser fit. Once done, my breasts and underarm lymph began breathing so much easier. I was sore under my left arm, but once I adjusted my bra, it went away. There wasn't any cancer in the lymph gland, it was just being choked and bruised by my bra. This soreness became more extreme when my body's metal toxicity caused the lymph to swell under my arms. One of the few things that gave my body relief was changing my habits regarding the way I wore bras.

After this experience, I read some research studies that suggest wearing an underwire bra is not healthy. They can cut off the circulation of our body's blood, lymph, and energy, preventing it from properly flowing. I recommend wearing camisoles, wearing your bra looser, or no longer wearing underwire bras. Alternatively, it is possible to purchase support bras made from breathable material that help improve your body's well-being. They can be found in an array of styles and sizes at specialty retailers.

Avoid Some Metals

Metals play an integral role in our body's well-being, but like nearly everything, moderation is key. Copper and iron are two of the most commonly known metals that our bodies need. Most metals can be found in the proper trace amounts in a healthy diet. However, not all metals all healthy for you, as some can detract from your health.

Did you know that most commercial antiperspirants contain aluminum? You may be rolling aluminum into your body everyday. Moreover, most women tend to shave their underarms and immediately apply an antiperspirant. This allows the aluminum a chance to go right into your lymphatic system through the lymph glands under your armpits. Just to remind you, your lymphatic system is a critical component of your immune system. Aluminum free deodorants can be found at most health food stores, some mass merchants, and over the internet. Take the time to read the label and look for ones that are aluminum free.

Another culprit for unwanted metals is aluminum foil and aluminum cookware. Appraise your cooking habits, and look for healthier alternatives.

Interestingly, over the counter medications can be one of the largest sources of aluminum. Frequent users of buffered aspirin, could possibly take up to 700 mg of this metal each day. Since aluminum contributes to bone damage, buffered aspirin can contribute to bone deterioration and arthritis. Digestive medicines such as diarrhea and hemorrhoid medicines can also contain aluminum. A typical dose of aluminum-containing antacids can contain as much as 200 mg. and an entire day's use can give you 800-5000 mg. of aluminum.

Heavy metals, a subset of metals, are generally not healthy for us at any level. Arsenic, mercury, and lead are the most recognizable heavy metals, but all heavy metals have down right scary effects on the human body. Heavy metal poisoning could result from contaminated drinking water, polluted air, especially near emission sources, or compromised food. Heavy metals are dangerous because they tend to accumulate in your body over time, especially when there isn't an ongoing cleansing program to manage the build up. Generally speaking, they are taken in and stored faster than your body is able to break them down (metabolize) or excrete them. Heavy metals can enter water supplies because of industrial and consumer waste, or from acidic rain, which breaks down soils, releasing heavy metals into streams, lakes, rivers, and groundwater.

Even if you annually participate in a cleansing/detoxing program and never knowingly ingested heavy metals, you are still at risk. It is possible for these metals to accumulate through the air you breathe and the food you eat. They can even permeate your skin.

Often heavy metal toxicity does not show physical symptoms during the early stages, making it even more difficult to diagnose. Even though physical symptoms may not appear, your body is still being damaged. This is what happened to me. I didn't show any of the normal symptoms for heavy metal toxicity, but the damage was already being done.

In February 2008, my second round of diagnostic tests showed improvement in all areas, including my intestinal health. However, there was one alarming result. My aluminum was at a toxic level of 157! The previous test done in August 2007 showed metals at 27, which was not good, but the priority was focusing on the parasite problem as it was literally eating my lunch. How did the levels reach 157 in just a few months? The members of the clinic that conducted the diagnostics and I felt that the detoxification process that I was undergoing for the tumor, shook loose metals that had been stored deep in my bones and ducts.

When I share this part of my journey, I am commonly asked how I got so much aluminum in my body. My guess is that my Mom used aluminum cookware when I was growing up. I also had years of using deodorant with aluminum, and years of using aluminum foil for grilling and baking foods. Combining this with any aluminum that my skin and body absorbed through drinking water, breathing air, and other environmental sources, and it becomes easy to imagine how a number could reach 157. For better health, I feel that using the helpful tool of diagnostics to discover the levels of heavy metals that your body is holding onto is of utmost importance. Once you are armed with this knowledge, you can create a game plan toward optimal health and well-being.

What if you feel okay? Should you still bother taking the time and spending the money on these diagnostic tests? Heavy metals accumulate in your body, so over time they could have a toxic effect which can greatly hinder your health, even if the cause is not known. When someone is sick, how many tests are run to determine metal toxicity? Not many.

Heavy metals can be very difficult to detox from and remove from your body's systems. My experience is that it took over seven months to eliminate the metals in my system, and it was quite painful. This was a harder process than getting rid of parasites, which are known as notoriously hard to get rid of.

Take the steps to stop putting heavy metals into your body. Be concerned of any food that is stored in an aluminum container. Start a cleansing program to rid your body of any heavy metals using the healing foods in previous sections and supplements, along with following the advice of health practitioners.

Plastic & Heat - Not a Good Combination

Sometimes, even the things that we think are ways to treat ourselves well and maintain health aren't as they seem. Recently plastics have taken the spotlight as one of those healthy tools gone wrong. For years, it has been suggested that bottled water is healthier, and although in some cases the water may be purer, the bottle can negate those benefits.

I used to drink spring water from plastic bottles, especially when I was on the go. It was easier to make water portable. However plastic that is left in a warm car or in the sun is at risk for becoming unhealthy. The plastic actually leeches into the water when it's hot. It seems like there is a new study every day that links plastics use to cancer. You may feel that your plastic water bottles are safe, because you always keep them cool or room temperature. Have you ever stepped onto a delivery truck? Most are not air conditioned unless it is for cold storage type foods or freezer items. I suggest that you stop using plastic water bottles, especially those exposed to heat. In addition, never drink from a plastic water bottle that has been left in a warm car.

The same thing is true for plastic wrap. How many times have you put some type of plastic in the microwave? Many people are even reevaluating their use of plastic-ware and are warning against placing it in the dishwasher. If you use any type of plastic in the kitchen, limit its exposure to heat and hand-wash it in lukewarm water. Be aware of heat and plastic, as they are proving to be an unhealthy combination.

Sunscreen

Recently I devoted the time to read all of the labels of my sunscreens. I was shocked to find out that most of them have ingredients that could be harmful to my health. Although sunscreens are FDA approved, research is showing that some approved active ingredients could disrupt hormones and increase free radicals, which can elevate the risk of skin cancer and hormone sensitive cancers.

Ingredients like octinoxate, homosalate, and oxybenzone can cause the effect of 'feeding' estrogen receptive cancers like breast and ovarian. They have also been linked to possible developmental abnormalities. Therefore, I would question their use with children or during pregnancy. These ingredients along with PABA, cinoxate, octisalate, and menthyl anthranilate can produce free radicals when they are absorbed in the skin. Free radicals in the skin can break down DNA and increase the risk of skin cancer – the very thing that sunscreens are supposed to help avoid. Several sunscreen manufacturers are starting to use nanoparticle-sized ingredients. These may not be on the label and are currently being investigated due to possible negative risks. Several countries have added warning labels on products that contain some of these ingredients or have banned their use.

I have decided to use products without these questionable ingredients. Some 'safe' products do exist, and I encourage you to research available options. I also invested the time to look at the labels of all of my skin lotions and creams, even though many did not include sunscreen. Surprisingly several had some of these ingredients. Check your labels out!

Interfacing with the Medical Community

Everything in this book can be utilized whether you choose traditional medical procedures, choose non-traditional procedures, or choose a combination of traditional and holistic care. Regardless of whether you decide to walk the non-traditional, traditional, or a combination path, I have some thoughts to help you along the way.

Natural Healing is Not Like Taking a Pill

Medical doctors are trained to prescribe medicines or treatments. That is why they are called Doctors of Medicine. I had two doctor friends share that they were not trained in nutrition, healing from the inside out, diet, or detoxification methods.

Therefore, if you embrace a path that incorporates non-traditional methods, you <u>may</u> meet resistance from the medical community simply because it is something that they are not knowledgeable about. Members of the medical community might tell you that you are taking a risk, or that your life is in danger. This can start to fill you with fear and doubt. It is important to know that most will have your best interests at heart, and are simply expressing their concern for you and your health. Even incorporating a routine for prevention and living well can sometimes cause concern from the traditional medical community.

Be prepared for this type of reaction so you are able to be strong within yourself, your own heart and soul, regarding whatever approach you decide upon. If you are not fully resolved and confident in the choice you make, your selected path, you could crumble and become fearful when interacting with the medical community. Generally speaking, they do not understand alternative health and healing approaches and will advise against them.

We all know that most medicines and treatments have possible negative side effects, and usually more than one or two. Today, so many of us are looking for alternative means that do not have these side effects. If you choose this path, it is not like taking a pill or cutting something out. That approach is a quick fix of the symptom, but may not permanently evoke change. The alternative healing approach supports your mind, body, and spirit to heal naturally. This is a more organic approach that evolves to a successful conclusion over a period of time. Everyone's journey is different, sometimes a brief amount of time is all that is needed, while other journeys can take longer and face unusual obstacles. If the body is maintained after successful healing with a healthy diet, healthy thoughts, and a healthy lifestyle, the issue should not return.

In 2001, I healed myself, using my own practice, of a lifetime of debilitating allergies, sinus infections, and vertigo. Today I live in the same environment that "caused" my allergies. I breathe the same air that bothered me before, and I have not had one symptom of allergies, sinus, or vertigo.

Similarly, a client of mine had great pain at the occipital ridge of her neck. She wore a neck brace every night and saw a chiropractor three times a week for over nine years. We worked together in August of 2004, and the pain has not returned. Both of these are examples of what I mean by a complete healing, where the issue does not return.

Alternative healing does not always offer a quick fix of a symptom, but it does offer a permanent healing that resonates beyond physical well-being. It creates a total uplift in attitude, enhanced spiritual awareness, and so much more that will change the way you appreciate life everyday. Embracing alternative healing by focusing on the cause and trusting the process as it unfolds will be a journey that can be trying or difficult at times, but it will always be extremely rewarding.

How Did I Interact with the Medical Community?

I never went back to the surgeon who told me that the gold standard was to cut out my entire left breast, lymph, and to follow up with chemotherapy and radiology. My lump was only the size of the top of my pinky finger. The doctor who did the biopsy told me that it appeared self-contained. The recommended gold standard approach seemed like overkill to me. That surgeon said that cancer never gets better, that it always gets worse. From my experience through my healing practice, I knew that this was not true. I looked into getting a second opinion at a hospital affiliated with a university. Why? Private practice doctors are paid when they do the procedures. Doctors working as part of a university or research hospital are paid the same whether they do the procedures or not. I believe this offers an opportunity for a more balanced recommendation. Also, these centers tend to be on the leading edge of medical innovation, and use experts in their field.

By the way, some of my comments are general statements. Physicians do exist that use a balanced approach and are open to alternative treatments. In my case, I could not locate one in my area, but network with your friends and family asking about their experiences with local doctors. Part of the premise of this section of the book was born from my Wellness Wisdom seminar. The feedback I received was that all of the information was important and beneficial, but what would stick in people's minds was how they do not have to do what the doctor says, the minute they say to do it. Depending on your situation, you can take a few days or even weeks to research other options. We are so programmed to believe unquestionably in doctors. We think that a doctor has all the information and knowledge, but they only have the wisdom and knowledge that they were trained in. For instance, a surgeon is primarily trained to do surgery. That is their area of expertise. They probably will not be knowledgeable in other areas.

It is important to reach out to a variety of medical professionals, alternative practitioners, and beyond for their expertise. That is why I formed my own healing plan, utilizing knowledge from all directions.

As I researched second opinions, I learned that if I had another biopsy, it could actually pull cancer through and into other parts of my body - not a good idea. Given that I no longer wanted a biopsy, there would be no way for me to prove that my work was having an impact and that the change I felt taking place in the lump was real. Although the energy of the lump was dormant and it was gradually getting smaller, it was still there.

At this point in my journey, I had to ask myself why I needed a second opinion. I knew I could heal myself using spiritual transformational healing at a cellular level, along with diet, supplements, support treatments, and protocols. I realized I wanted medical proof of my success and that it was not possible at that time. I never doubted God, my angels, or my guides, but I suddenly doubted myself. This seems unlikely as I help others to heal everyday. I trust without doubt that when God sends someone to me, that I can help him or her. There is no doubt. However, I found myself in doubt, wanting that proof.

I turned to a select few in the healing arts to support me in putting my doubts to bed. Once done, I chose no interaction with the medical community, except for diagnostic tools like screening, blood and bowel tests, etc. I courageously walked my path as the general contractor for my health and the inner physician for myself, with God as my guidance and my source of wisdom and direction.

About two months later, I learned about a thermogram, which is a healthy alternative to mammograms as no radiation is used. (See section on 'Screening: Thermogram', page 113.) I had two scans done three months apart that showed no indications of cancer and no negative change to my breast tissue 'thumbprint'. These positive results have continued with every subsequent thermogram.

When I went to my annual GYN exam about 10 months after the diagnosis of cancer, I was not well received. The interaction was one that filled me with fear. I was told that I was making a mistake. I asked, "Did you see the thermogram reports? They showed no cancer." I was diligently sending copies of the thermograms to my medical doctors. My GYN told me that she didn't feel good about it. She proceeded to knead my breast for over five minutes trying to find the lump, but could not find it. Even though there was no lump, I was still told that I was making a mistake. I was there to have two pap tests done, one for the cervix and one for the vagina. I was asked, "What will you do when the pap tests show that you still have dysplasia of the vagina and virus of the cervix?" I was diagnosed with this about two months prior to the cancer diagnosis and had done the work to heal it. I suggested that we wait to see the results. Both tests came back 'normal'. Even though this exchange was disconcerting, the exam and diagnostics showed continued proof of my healing success in both parts of my body.

I want to add that when I researched and interacted with doctors affiliated with a teaching or university hospital, they were more open to talking about alternative approaches, in conjunction with their treatments. In addition, they didn't recommend that all procedures needed to be done, unlike the first private practice doctor that I met with. There was a wait and see, or a gradual approach, before we do 'all treatments'.

Radiology and chemotherapy have such drastic side effects on your body. I know someone who used chemotherapy to address a tumor in his spine. Although this got rid of it for the moment, he became paralyzed on one side of his body. Several years later, the tumor grew back. So, this time radiology was done and that crippled the use of both of his legs. This person is no longer able to walk, even with support, and has constant pain. Then he was told that nothing else could be done. The worst part was that the radiology had no impact on the tumor - it remained in place.

Another person I know had breast cancer that metastasized to her spine. These same treatments were done, leaving her with a deformed spine. She used to walk straight and tall, and now she is bent over. Often there is no choice when the disease is so widespread, but pause before you jump when it is not widespread. If my condition did not get better after my approach, I would have gotten a lumpectomy without the other treatments. I knew if I healed the cause (mental/emotional), it would not grow back.

How Did I Use the Medical Community?

I used a holistic clinic that had several medical doctors, as well as a naturopathic doctor, and a physicist, to do detailed diagnostics. The gift of diagnostics (work-ups of the blood, bowel, skin, urine, etc) helped pinpoint what parts of the body to focus on with transformational healing, diet, nutrition, and detoxification. There were no medical doctors in my area that would perform these diagnostic tests and provide tailored recommendations for detoxification and supplementation. I drove six hours to work with the holistic clinic closest to me, and it was worth it. The support was invaluable.

I also used the medical community as part of the thermogram process, as three medical doctors review and assess it. I used the medical community for my annual GYN exam. I continue to use the medical community for annual tests and diagnostics. That is where their benefit lies for me.

When You are Prescribed Medicine that You Do Not Feel Comfortable Taking

I found out a few years ago from a proactive bone scanning diagnostic that I had pre-early osteoporosis. I was given a prescription, but I never filled it. I decided to do my own transformational healing work to remove the buried cause, which was feeling unsupported. I continued to be religious about walking and doing resistance training primarily though Pilates, both of which are known to be good prevention tools for osteoporosis. I also made sure I had the proper amount of calcium and magnesium each day and increased the amount of zinc and vitamin D supplements to my routine to help improve calcium absorption. I regularly said my affirmations and visualized by bones as dense and healthy. In one year, the bone loss not only stopped progressing, it had actually improved. My Doctor said 'I am sure glad you took that medicine,' and gave me another prescription. I just smiled, took the prescription, and never said anything.

I am sharing this not because I recommend that you do as I did, but because I have learned that sometimes it is best not to share everything. If I had said something to the doctor like, "I used other healing approaches," it might have created a confrontational exchange. What was a pleasant office visit could have become something else entirely.

My final advice is to not make decisions quickly, or when you are in fear or doubt. Remember that it is always within your right at all times to ask questions and to get answers to your questions. If you are not comfortable or unsure about something, get other opinions. Consult with other health care professionals, medical doctors, or alternative care practitioners. Take the time to do your own research. Network and contact others who have had similar health issues and used different approaches. Many people with diseases find themselves rushed into immediate drastic procedures when their situation is one of early detection or is self-contained. For many conditions, a few weeks or a few days will not make a big difference on their health and well-being. Take that time to pause. Know the timeline for your situation, if you have a few days, use those as best as you can. Even if you are in a dire situation, a few hours almost always can be taken to think things through and receive guidance from God.

Give yourself the space and time to think it through with your heart, as well as your mind. When you have this perspective, whatever approach you decide upon will be the right one. However, always address the cause of your health issue (the buried emotional, mental cause), and support your body's ability to heal or recover with diet, nutrition, detoxification, breathing, and sleep.

Supporting a Traditional Medical Approach

Although I chose a natural approach to heal breast cancer, I help many who choose a traditional path. I have worked with several clients who wanted support to help ensure a successful surgery, address the spiritual or emotional cause, facilitate a complete healing so further medication or procedures wouldn't be required, or help minimize the negative impact of radiology and chemotherapy.

Of course, a healthy diet and exercise routine, along with holding positive thoughts and emotions is always important to maintain health.

Surgery Support

Clients who I work with before and after surgery share that they experienced amazingly brief recoveries without pain. Their doctors are always amazed and tell them that it is very unusual.

The focus of these sessions can be varied as the needs of every client and every surgery vary. Common threads include work that:

- Energetically clears buried issues from the area of the body that is receiving surgery, to support successful surgery and recovery.
- Communicates with the body to let it know what will be happening, so it is prepared.
- Asks spiritual helpers to be at the surgeon's side to guide and to protect.
- Guides imagery of the wound's fast healing without pain or itching, and with minimal scaring.
- Boosts the immune system with energetic work.

Healing While Under Medical Care

Healing the buried emotional, mental cause is critical, and it can be done while on medication or undergoing medical procedures. After experiencing sessions targeting the cause of high blood pressure, my clients often go from high blood pressure to low blood pressure. Why? Their medication! When their blood pressure becomes normal due to our work, their medication is still doing its job so they begin to have low blood pressure. Doctors of two clients have said, 'Let's get you off this for a few days and see how it goes.' Neither client has needed to go back to their old medications.

Another client was experiencing an increased heart rate. It used to be in the 70's. Then it increased to the 90's and then to the 110's. She was planning on seeing her doctor and was going to ask for a prescription. Before she did this, we had a session together working on the emotional and mental cause of the increased heartbeat. During our session, she physically felt her heart beat slowing. Afterwards, she tested her heart rate and it was down to 79. The next morning it was 72. It has maintained itself in the 70's, just where it used to be. She is thrilled that this work prevented her from having to take medication.

A client with stage 4 kidney failure was still taking the same medicines that she had been on for years for this, and other health issues. It is common for people with kidney failure to have a build up of toxic fluids and associated tissue swelling throughout their body. After we worked together, she noticed a reduction of the swelling in her body and started monitoring her fluid count. When I saw her two weeks later, she looked great. She had lost most of the excess, toxic fluid weight. She told me she felt terrific. About a month later, when she was in the hospital for a 'possible stroke', the doctor checked in on her kidney to see if it was linked to the problem. She was told by the surprised doctor that her kidneys looked really good! The only thing that she did differently was the work with me. While under medical care over the last several years, her situation went from stage 1 kidney failure to stage 4. She was told dialysis would be the next step if the deterioration continued. She has diligently chosen to continue taking the prescribed meditations, but she has also chosen to work at healing the root cause with me. It isn't necessary for her to stop taking her medications in order to work in the transformational healing arena. At her most recent check-up with her doctor of five years, she was told, "I can't explain this, but it looks like your kidney failure is reversing. Your stage 4 failure is now at stage 2." Initially, it took her a long time to decide to work with me, but she is now very pleased that she stepped out and tried something new.

Another client had a brain CT scan that showed a dark golf ball size mass. She took a medication that helped to prevent blood clotting and decided to work with me. In our session, we worked to facilitate the transformational energy healing for her brain mass. It was only about a week later, when the doctors did another CT scan. She called me excited to report that her condition had drastically changed, as the dark mass now appeared as scar tissue with new healthy cells growing around it. This was exactly what we focused on in our guided imagery work. We told her body that the mass was going away and that new cells were growing in to replace it. Currently, her doctors are discussing taking her off the prescription for blood clotting.

When someone has a health condition, which has been a part of them for a while, they become accustomed to their body behaving in a certain way. It is always interesting to notice the immediate physical changes that this work brings about for them. A client who has prostate cancer experienced an immediate and extremely large release through urine. He started to work with me while going through the medical treatments for prostate cancer. He had always had difficulty urinating and tended only to be able to urinate in small amounts, creating the need to urinate frequently. In our first session, we released the negative energy that was buried in his prostate from childhood experiences. Afterwards, he shared that he had urinated easily and in a much larger amount. He said he thought it was never going to stop. Interestingly, he had urinated right before the session started, so it was hard to understand where this came from. I knew, from my experience working with others, that this was his body's way of releasing the cellular density from his buried, childhood wounds. This density actually contributed to his difficulty urinating. What a cleansing experience! He has continued to go through the recommended medical treatments and has the energy to maintain a busy career and life.

For another client, it started when she experienced a shortness of breath and difficulty walking up and down stairs. Her breathing would be so strained that she would become dangerously dizzy. Medical scans showed large dark spots on her lungs, indicating cancer. She chose chemotherapy and immediately called for a session with me. After one long intense session, she received her full breath back. The difference was noticeable to both of us during the session. A couple of days later, she emailed to share that she could easily walk up and down stairs. At the end of the week, she was back on stage singing in a musical production. Previously she had pulled out of the show because she did not have the breath to sing. She was delighted!

We did another brief session as she felt a slight heaviness when she focused on her breath. We found the buried energy of fear. She was fearful that the shortness would return. We worked to transform that fear into faith and confidence. A subsequent CT scan showed that the dark spots on her lungs were miniscule in size.

Remember, you do not have to stop using your prescribed medical approach for transformational healing to help you. In fact, they can be very complementary. Holistic care and medical care are not exclusive from each other. I hope that this will be the way of the future.

Minimizing the Effects of Chemotherapy & Radiology

There are times when a disease is so aggressive, that radical approaches are needed. Chemo and radiology have their place in modern medicine, helping many to live longer lives. Medical intervention and transformational healing can work together to create a whole healing.

One of my clients had a hysterectomy to remove a rare and aggressive form of cancer that had also metastasized to her liver. She immediately began an aggressive chemotherapy regimen to prevent further cancer growth. When I started working with her, a second phase of treatment that included two high dose chemotherapy infusions had been scheduled. Each treatment required a stem cell transplant to help her immune system recover, because the chemo would make it nearly nonexistent.

We did several sessions finding the root mental, emotional cause of her disease and transformed it. We focused heavily on her liver, as this area had not been surgically addressed. She did not want any additional surgical procedures. She did a lot of guided imagery work in meditations to support the work that we were doing together. Follow-up scans showed that she was in complete remission. She had been told that because of the type of cancer she had, she would have to be in remission before the two scheduled high dose chemos and stem cell transplants could happen. Because this type of cancer has a high reoccurrence rate due to "micromets" floating in the blood, remission of the liver cancer was needed in order to have the best chance for overall success. She worked hard to make this remission happen without surgery. She did a session with me every week and diligently worked with her positive affirmations and visualized her successful outcome.

She proceeded with the high dose chemo and stem cell replacement. A healthy immune system was vitally important to moving forward and we both knew that chemo would have a taxing, negative effect. We worked together before each high dose chemo treatment to transform any buried issues and their related density from the immune system. We also worked to clear any prior negative effects from the previous chemotherapy treatments, so she could start each treatment with a clear, healthy immune system. After the first heavy dose of chemo, we took an inventory of her immune system. As expected, it was a wreck and totally dysfunctional. In fact, the lymphatic system showed itself to her as a highway with multiple car wrecks and nothing was moving. We cleared the 'accidents' so the lymph could flow again and prepared the body to receive the infusion of stem cells.

Then there was a waiting period. The doctors looked at her white blood cell count to indicate if her stem cells had engrafted. Her count would have to go up before she would be allowed to return home from the hospital. We did a session were the bone marrow showed itself as a subway car full of white blood cells, but the doors wouldn't open. We opened the doors and the blood cells raced out. The next morning, her white blood cell count not only had recovered, but it was higher than what was needed.

After all of the procedures were complete, she went to a hospital clinic daily, for check ups. During this period, she was concerned about the level of the absolute neutrophils, a specific segment of white blood cells. The doctors did not like the low level of 1.34. Also, the total white count was at 2.4. We did work to target the neutrophils level within her body. The day after our work together, she called from the hospital excited that the absolute neutrophils went up from 1.34 to 2.26, and the total white count rose from 2.4 to 3.9!

She told me that she is grateful for the support of my practice, and for helping her learn how to change the patterns that caused her serious health issues. Although she is a professional in the medical field, she is a strong advocate of blending traditional medicine with alternative healing modalities. From the beginning, she embraced a supportive routine of nutrition, meditation, and exercise. Today she is healthy and vibrant. She has even incorporated the healing practices that she learned while working with me into her everyday life. Like me, she says she will never go back to her old way of being, living, and eating.

Conclusion:

All of the above clients have two things in common. They used traditional medical procedures, while working with me, and they feel changed – spiritually, mentally, emotionally, and physically.

Just like me, they feel lighter, calmer, happier, and spiritually aligned. We realize now that there are benefits to having diseases and health issues like wonderful spiritual lessons and insights that will support us for the remainder of our lives. We all learned new tools that we can use to maintain our health and well-being. We all learned the importance of relaxing and enjoying life moment, by moment, with joy.

Wellness Wisdom Tips from Alice

- Do not make decisions quickly when in fear.
- Do not re-biopsy.
- Never claim your disease, health issue, or unwanted life situation.
- If possible, use doctors associated with educational hospitals versus those in private practice.
- Set your intention – all follows intention!
- Master your thoughts, focus on the positive, and what you want. Act and feel like it is occurring.
- Ask for help
- Share with and surround yourself with people who will support you without fear and doubt. Limit who you tell so you have time to heal.
- Do the spiritual, mental, emotional healing at a cellular level to address the cause, regardless of what type of medical or holistic methods you choose to use.
- Know that you are on your soul's journey. Know that you will succeed. All healing is spiritual first.
- If you look for it, negative experiences, including sickness and disease, represent a gift for you.
- Visualize what you want to occur. Feel the feelings as if it is already occurring.
- Draw and journal your healing work, intentions, and creation work, to help manifest it.
- Stop using plastic in the microwave and dishwasher. Don't leave plastic bottles in the car, or sun.
- Use medical diagnostics of saliva, urine, bowel, blood, and gastro to guide your eating, supplement, and healing routine. Diagnostic results aid you to heal yourself from the inside out.
- Change your diet and nutrition now, so you won't foster known or unknown disease. Place a focus on eating to maintain a healthy intestinal environment.
- Get plenty or sleep and rest. Your body heals and restores while sleeping.
- Use at least one of these (meditation, yoga, Pilates, or Qigong) to keep yourself balanced and centered, along with oxygenating your cells.
- Choose a holistic practice to support your body's natural healing. I chose acupuncture.
- Make the health of your lymph a priority with supplements and physical movements.
- Stop using aluminum foil. Use aluminum free deodorant.
- Consider vibrational protocols to support you body's healing.
- Stop using underwire bras. Loosen non-underwire bras.
- Use cleansing and detoxing protocols to remove environmental toxins and metals from your body.
- Use a thermogram for prevention scanning, instead of radiology.
- Establish a healthy home and site environment.

Positive Affirmations for Breast Cancer

Good for Healing & Prevention!

- I love and respect myself
- I am proud of who I am
- I am clean and pure
- I nourish and support myself
- I am emotionally nourished and supported by others
- I am perfect just as I am
- I am worthy
- I am acknowledged and respected
- I am gentle with myself and I honor myself
- It is okay to make mistakes
- It is okay to take time for me
- I allow myself to put myself first
- I allow myself the time and space to heal
- I love my breasts
- My breasts are whole and perfect
- All tissue in my breasts are normal and healthy
- My breasts are healed and whole
- I am healthy breasts; I am healthy body
- My immune system functions in an optimum manner
- I am happy and joyful
- I trust the process of my healing
- I am connected and aligned with my soul
- I am one with God; I am one with the Universe; I am one

Practices to Support Your Affirmations

- Send love to your breasts. Gently massage them. Tell them you love them.
- Visualize your cancer shrinking to nothing.
- Visualize the tissue of your breasts as healthy, normal tissue
- Visualize a Pac-man eating your cancer.
- Ask you breasts to show you what they look like now. Then ask them to show you what they look like as healed and whole. Hold the second image with gratitude.

Appendix: Before & After

I. My Reports: Biopsy & Thermograms

I am happy to share my reports that state my medical diagnosis from my biopsy (7/5/2007) and results from my thermograms after healing as described in this book. I have had a clean bill of health since 11/5/2007. The scan on 11/5/2007, just four months after the biopsy, showed no white or red heat at the 10 o'clock position of my left breast, which is where the biopsy had showed a cancerous tumor. In fact, my entire breast was a nice cool color of blue, indicating healthy tissue.

Before: My Biopsy Report July 2007

Patient Name: **MCCALL, ALICE J**

RM Bed:	Accession #:
Location: PHYSICIAN'S OFFICE	Collected: 6/29/2007
Billing #:	Received: 7/2/2007
	Reported: 7/5/2007

Specimen(s) Received
LEFT BREAST BIOPSY

Pre-Operative Diagnosis
LEFT BREAST NODULE

Gross Description
"McCall – left breast biopsy." The specimen is received in formalin and consists of three grayish white needle core fragments measuring 0.3 cm to 1.0 cm. Processed in their entirety in cassette A1-3.   DH/PT/kdh 07/02/07

Final Pathologic Diagnosis
LEFT BREAST BIOPSY:
-   SMALL CYLINDRICAL FRAGMENTS OF DENSE FIBROUS TISSUE SHOWING GRADE II INFILTRATING DUCTAL CARCINOMA COMPRISING SOME 60% OF THE BIOPSY SPECIMEN.
-   NO DEFINITE CHANGES OF VASCULAR OR LYMPHATIC INVASION IDENTIFIED.
-   IMMUNOPEROXIDASE STAINS FOR HORMONE RECEPTOR STATUS ARE PENDING.

Comment
These immunohistochemical stains were performed on formalin fixed, paraffin embedded tissue. ER antibody clone is CF11, PR antibody clone is 1E2, and HER-2/neu antibody clone is 4B5. All procedures use an I-View DAB detection system.

GDC/PT/tmj   07/03/07

AMENDED REPORT – RESULTS OF ADDITIONAL STAINS:

The amended report is issued to report immunoperoxidase stains for hormone receptor status.

The following results are obtained:

Estrogen receptor: Positive in 90+% of tumor cells.
Progesterone receptor: Positive in 80+% of tumor cells examined.
HER-2/neu excess surface antigenicity: 0-1+ (negative result).

After: My Thermogram Results: November 2007

The color of my entire left breast was blue, a sign of healthy tissue. Also, no defined vascular patterns were noted, meaning that there was no indication of cancer. It was recommended that I have a thermogram three months later as a precaution because of the recent biopsy and diagnosis of DCIS – Ductal Carcinoma Breast Cancer.

REPORT

Patient: Alice McCall

Scan Date: 11/5/2007

Report Type: Breast
Thermographer: Carol Cunningham

All normal protocols were observed

HISTORY AND SUBJECTIVE COMPLAINTS:

Ms. McCall   reports the following: Previous illness:
 allergies which have been resolved; Previous surgery: tonsilectomy at 3 yrs. old;
Current health problem: diagnosed on 7/9/07 with estrogen and progesterone
receptive DCIS at 10 o'clock in the left breast. She states her mother was a breast
cancer survivor. Medication: none. Other treatment: diet, supplements, spiritual
energy healing, meditation, acupuncture, rest, qigeng, yoga, essential oils,
detoxification, colon hydrotherapy, etc.

THERMOGRAPHIC INTERPRETATION:

There are mild thermal asymmetries noted in the breasts. Diffuse thermal patterns
are noted in both breasts, L>R. An area of slight hyperthermia is noted at the 10
o'clock region of the left upper inner breast, and may correspond to the previous
biopsy site. No defined vascular patterns are noted. This area should be closely
monitored given the known diagnosis of DCIS. There are no discreet thermal
findings in the right breast.
This study is suitable to be archived and compared with a repeat study in 3 months
to form a baseline for annual comparative study.

DISCUSSION:
The thermal findings in the right breast are considered to be low risk for significant
developing pathology at this time.
The thermal findings in the left breast are considered to be at high risk for
developing pathology with a known diagnosis of DCIS, and close clinical and thermal
monitoring is suggested until a clear baseline is established.
The reported lumps in the left breast may relate to the DCIS or possibly fibrocystic
changes.

FOLLOW-UP:
Suggest follow-up breast imaging in three months before continuing with annual
comparative studies.

PROCEDURE:
This patient was examined with digital infrared thermal imaging to identify thermal
findings which may suggest abnormal physiology.

Continued Health: My Thermogram Results: March 2009

This report includes a summary showing that I have had healthy breast tissue from 11/2007 through 3/2009.

REPORT

Patient: Alice McCall

Scan Date: 3/8/2009

Report Type: Full Body + Breast
Thermographer: Carol Cunningham

All normal protocols were observed

HISTORY AND SUBJECTIVE COMPLAINTS:

This is a breast follow-up from 9/26/08, 2/6/08, and 11/5/07 + full body. She reports no changes to her previously reported breast health history. She further reports that she sometimes has some right sided sciatica but is currently experiencing no pain.

THERMOGRAPHIC INTERPRETATION:

BREAST:
There are no significant thermal changes seen in this follow-up study as compared to 11/5/2007, 2/6/2008, and 9/26/2008. Thermal patterns and temperature differentials have remained stable in both breasts (for the breast studies done on both 3/7/2009 and 3/8/2009).
The long term stability of all thermal patterns continue to show a reliable comparative record of stable physiology with no indication of tissue changes. This study is suitable for archiving and continues to be regarded as reliable for future comparative analysis.

II. A Client's Before & After Thermogram

One of my clients learned about thermograms from me, and decided to start using it for early detection. In September of 2008, the thermogram showed that her breasts were fine, but it uncovered a hot spot in the upper left side of her back. She had no pain there, so she was unaware of a problem. She had another scan done in March of 2009 to check in on it. The only thing she did in between was two healing sessions with me. We worked to identify and transform the root cause, at a cellular and subconscious level. We also did some direct energetic bodywork. She did her part by saying her positive affirmations regularly. The results shown below are dramatic. There is no sign of any hot spot and her entire back is a nice cool shade of green. The second scan did uncover another problem with her neck, which we immediately worked on. We both know that proof of that transformation will be found on her next thermogram.

Before: A Client's Thermogram (9/08) of Her Back
Notice the Hot Spot on Upper Left Back

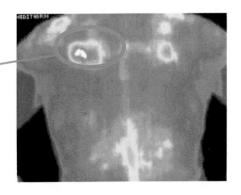

After: Thermogram (3/09)
The Hot Spot is Gone & is Now a Healthy Green!

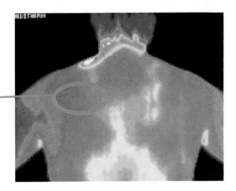

III. A Client's Verbal Report from Her Doctor

Before
An MRI was done on this client's brain in mid January 2009, due to possible stroke. She was shown the film from the MRI and saw a golf ball size dark mass in the left side of her brain. The doctors were not sure what caused it, but they gave her a prescription to help prevent clots from forming in the blood.

After
We had one session together to work on this issue, about one week before her next scheduled MRI in March 2009. The doctor told her that the scan showed no dark mass, but instead scar tissue where the mass had been located with new cells growing around it. This is exactly what we visualized as part of our deep healing work.

IV. A Client's Medical Reports Related to Lymphoma

Although diagnosed with stage 3 lymphoma, non-curable, this client did not engage in the typical medical treatments of chemotherapy or radiology. She embraced a regime of working with me to heal the root cause at a cellular and subconscious level. Her routine also included Chinese herbs and acupuncture. She was given a clean bill of health approximately eight months after diagnosis, and her semi-annual visits to a lymphoma specialist show that her condition remains stable.

Before

This client's first tests showed an alarmingly high white blood cell count: 70.80 versus the normal range of 4.49 - 11.69. Neutrophils, lymphocytes and hemoglobin, which are other components of healthy blood, were also out of the normal range. The report below was conducted on 3/22/06.

```
                                        COLLECTED: 03/22/2006-2:00PM
                                        RECEIVED: 03/23/2006-5:09PM
                                        REPORTED: 03/24/2006-4:19AM
```

Test Name	Within Range	Outside Range	Normal Range	Units
CBC				
WBC		70.80 (CH)	4.49-11.69	THOU/CUMM
WBC CHECKED				
RBC		4.05 (L)	4.11-5.13	MILL/CUMM
HEMOGLOBIN		10.4 (L)	11.7-15.5	GMS
HEMATOCRIT		32.1 (L)	35.6-44.9	%
MCV		79.4 (L)	80.6-93.6	FL
MCH		25.8 (L)	26.7-32.3	PG
MCHC		32.5 (L)	32.6-36.0	G/DL
RDW		18.8 (H)	12.0-13.8	%
PLATELET COUNT	213		159-373	THOU/CUMM
NEUTROPHILS		2.5 (L)	44.8-74.2	%
LYMPHOCYTES		95.4 (H)	16.8-44.2	%
FEW SMUDGE CELLS				
MONOCYTES		1.6 (L)	2.0-13.0	%
EOSINOPHILS	0.5		0-5.1	%
BASOPHILS	0.0		0-1.2	%
SED RATE (WESTERGREN)		25 (H)	0-20	MM/HR
TSH	3.38		0.27-4.2	uIU/ML

*** FINAL REPORT ***

Interim – Our Work Together

Her white blood cell count was our primary concern, so I focused the majority of the transformational energy healing work on finding and addressing the cause of the increased white blood cells. Only a moderate amount of time was spent on the affected lymph glands, nodes, and spleen. In just three months, this client experienced a reduction in the size of the lymph glands in her neck. They not only felt smaller to her touch, but to her doctor's touch as well.

On 8/3/2006, she returned for another round of tests. The results showed dramatic improvement with her white blood cell count. Previously the count was 70,000, but these new tests revealed a count of 9,000, which is within a normal, healthy range. This report also showed us that it was time to place emphasis on the affected lymph nodes and spleen. Over the next three months, we used an array of energy healing modalities to effect the change that we desired. This work included direct bodywork on the immune system and guided imagery on the affected areas of the body.

The following are excerpts from the 8/3/2006 report.

Date of Visit: 08/03/2006

PROGRESS NOTE
Hematologic Malignancy Clinic

IDENTIFICATION: Ms   is a 43-year-old woman with a diagnosis of marginal
cell lymphoma.

INTERVAL HISTORY: Ms   returns to clinic for followup of her marginal
cell lymphoma. Since her last visit, she has been feeling well with no B
symptoms including fevers or chills weight loss, night sweats, changes in
energy.

She has had no medical complications since her last visit. If anything, she
states that her lymph nodes in her neck have decreased in size over the
past 3 months. This morning, she underwent a CT scan, which shows the
presence of persistent diffuse lymphadenopathy with centimeter-sized nodes
in the neck and larger lymph nodes in the axilla. There are several
perimesenteric, periaortic lymph nodes in the abdomen that measure up to 7
cm in aggregate and there are some large iliac and peri-inguinal lymph
nodes as well. Her spleen is extremely large at 25 cm craniocaudally,
extending well below the pelvic rim. Two incidental lung nodules smaller
than 1 cm in size were also noted.

REVIEW OF SYSTEMS: Please see HPI. All other systems are negative in detail.

PHYSICAL EXAM: The patient's vital signs include a weight 57.7 kg,
temperature of 97.5, blood pressure 118/78, pulse of 82 and a respiratory
rate of 18. On general appearance, this is a well-developed, well-nourished
woman sitting comfortably in no acute distress. HEENT: Sclerae anicteric.
Pupils are equal, round and reactive to light. Extraocular movements
intact. Mucous membranes moist without oral lesions or exudate. Neck is
supple with multiple subcentimeter lymph nodes felt in the posterior
cervical chain. There is a 2-cm lymph node palpable on the right axilla and
a 1.5-cm lymph node palpable on the left axilla. Cardiac: Regular rate and
rhythm, S1 and S2 without murmurs, rubs or gallops. Chest: Clear to
auscultation bilaterally. Abdomen: Soft and nontender with spleen that
encompasses the entire left hemi-abdomen. Extremities are without cyanosis,
clubbing or edema. Neurologic: The patient is alert and oriented x 3 with
no focal neurologic deficits.

DATA REVIEW: Laboratory values reveal normal electrolytes, creatinine and
liver function tests. Her complete blood count reveals a white blood cell
count of 9000, which is down from 70,000 reported prior to her last visit.
Her hemoglobin is still low at 10.5 gm/dL giving her a hematocrit of 32.7%.
The platelets are 207,000, her MCV is 72.8. The differential on her white
count reveals 54% lymphocytes, 38% polys with 1 atypical cell and no
blasts.

After

In November of 2006, she returned to her doctor for another round of tests. The results of her vital statistics not only showed that she is healthier than when the previous tests were taken, but it showed that she was in better shape than most people her age. Even more impressive was the news that there were no signs of lymphoma and that all lymph glands and the spleen were back to normal size and functioning well.

These positive results occurred without chemotherapy, radiation, or traditional medications. Three years later, her white blood count, hemoglobin, neutrophils, and lymphocytes are all in normal range. Below is her most recent report from 3/12/09.

Hematology Report

Collected: 03/12/2009 09
Received : 03/12/2009 09

Test Description	Result	Flags	Ref. Range	Units
WBC COUNT	5.8		(3.8-9.2)	(K/UL)
RBC COUNT	4.71		(3.8-5.0)	(M/UL)
HEMOGLOBIN	14.0		(11.9-15.0)	(GM/DL)
HEMATOCRIT	41.1		(34.8-43.6)	(%)
MCV	87.2		(81-97)	(FL)
MCH	29.8		(27.6-33.9)	(PG)
MCHC	34.1		(33.3-35.4)	(%)
RDW	15.2	H	(11.5-14.8)	(%)
PLATELET	267		(155-410)	(K/UL)
BLAST	0			(%)
NEUTROPHILS	67		(49-79)	(%)
EO	2		(0-6)	(%)
BASO	1		(0-1)	(%)
LYMPHS	22		(11-38)	(%)
MONO	8		(5-12)	(%)
ABS NEUTROPHILS	3.88		(2.0-6.4)	(K/UL)
ABS BLASTS	0.00			(K/UL)
ABS EOS	0.12		(0.0-0.4)	(K/UL)
ABS BASOS	0.06		(0.0-0.1)	(K/UL)
ABS LYMPHS	1.28		(0.5-2.6)	(K/UL)
ABS MONOS	0.46		(0.2-0.9)	(K/UL)

RBC MORPHOLOGY
    SLIGHT ANISOCYTOSIS
    SLIGHT MICROCYTES

PLT MORPHOLOGY   WITHIN NORMAL LIMITS

Flag Key: L (Abnormally Low)   H (Abnormally High)   C (Corrected)
    LL (Critically Low)   HH (Critically High)
Prior to 07/29/2004 ** (Critically Abnormal)   C (Corrected)

V. <u>A Client's Medical Reports Related to Multiple Sclerosis</u>

This client had severe numbness, burning, and pain throughout her body, especially related to her spine. Several MRIs were done on the brain, the cervical spine, and thoracic spine, with and without contrast, in June 2007. After given a lumbar puncture, she was told that Multiple Sclerosis was the cause. Over the next two years, she was given different shots and medications to reduce pain. She was also told that this type of physical condition does not get better.

Although we worked together a couple of times during my healing journey in 2007, she committed to work with me starting in the summer of 2008. We worked on a regular basis, with some breaks, for about eight months.

The emphasis of our work was on the emotional, mental cause, which came from this lifetime and multiple past lives. The common link across these lifetimes was physical issues with the spine and head. After we cleared her buried emotional density from these lifetimes, we did a lot of work on the brain and the spine below the cervical area. We worked on energetically rebuilding the entire spine, with lots of focus on rewiring the spine, including the connection from the brain. This was done to improve the overall spinal signal. Her diagnostic tests showed that her spinal signal was not functioning. We also included work with the spinal fluid. After this work, her pain was greatly reduced, but we were still working on her complete healing. It was about this time that she had another set of MRIs (4/14/2009).

She had multiple MRIs in 2007 and 2009. There are too many reports to include here, so I am sharing the comparison report from 4/14/2009, as it states the difference in the condition from 2007 to 2009.

Before & After Comparison of MRIs of the Brain:

In 2007, the MRI of the brain, with and without contrast, showed abnormal white matter in the frontal regions, which was 6.5mm in size suggesting the possibility of demyelization. Demyelization is the major underlying factor responsible for the symptoms of multiple sclerosis (MS). It is the destructive removal of myelin, an insulating protective fatty protein that sheaths nerve cells (neurons). A loss of myelin often shows up as white patches in the central nervous system. No wonder she was experiencing burning, numbness, and pain.

There is marked improvement in the 2009 report below. Most significant, is that the size of abnormal matter went from 6.5mm to 2.3mm.

```
                              REPORT STATUS: Final
    PATIENT:             SHANA


    SERVICE PROVIDED ON:   04/14/2009@1414



    -----------------------------------------------------------


    NON-AFFILIATE INFO:

            PROCEDURE
            MR BRAIN W&W/O CONTRAST
    -----------------------------------------------------------
```

MRI brain with and without contrast dated 4/14/2009

Clinical history: Multiple sclerosis. Numbness. Back pain.

Comparison: 6/8/2007.

Previously seen abnormal focus involving the right frontal lobe perirectal white matter has decreased in size. Previously this was 6.5 mm. Now this measures 2.3 mm. There are a few tiny foci along the posterior frontal lobe and posterior carpus callosum. These are very subtle. There is a tiny, 2 mm size new focus in the right posterior temporal lobe white matter. No other new foci identified. There is no acute hemorrhage, acute infarction, midline shift, extraaxial fluid collection, abnormal enhancement or enhancing mass. The ventricular system is within normal limits.

Impression:
1. Interval marked decrease in the size of the right frontal lobe demyelinating plaque.
2. Stable foci along the periventricular white matter. However there is a new tiny focus identified in the right posterior temporal lobe white matter. This could be a new small demyelinating plaque. Clinical correlation recommended. No abnormal enhancement, no acute infarct.

Before & After Comparison of MRIs of the Thoracic Spine:

In 2007, the MRI of the thoracic spine, with and without contrast, showed a discrete lesion within the thoracic cord at T-2. A spinal lesion, also often referred to as a tumor, is an abnormal substance that usually inhibits spinal functioning. In addition, an area of altered signal was noted. Spinal signal refers to the energy or current that flows from the brain to the spine and out to your body through the entire nervous system. Altered signal simply means that it is not functioning correctly, which could be a cause of numbness, pain, and burning. The conclusion of this report was an abnormal thoracic cord with possible demyelinating disease and degenerative disk disease.

There is marked improvement in the 2009 report below, including no abnormal cord signal, resolution of the lesion at T-2, and no evidence of demyelization. Only minimal degenerative disk disease was seen on this report.

```
                                  REPORT STATUS: Final
     PATIENT:        . SHANA


     SERVICE PROVIDED ON:  04/14/2009@1415




     ------------------------------------------------------------------------


     NON-AFFILIATE INFO:

              PROCEDURE
              MR SPINE THOR W&W/O CONTR
     ------------------------------------------------------------------------
```

MRI THORACIC SPINE WITHOUT AND WITH CONTRAST 4/14/2009

CLINICAL HISTORY: Multiple sclerosis. Numbness. Back pain.

COMPARISON: 6/6/2007.

TECHNICAL FACTORS: Multiplanar, multisequence imaging of the thoracic spine without and with contrast.

FINDINGS: Previously seen abnormal cord signal at T2 level is no longer identified. There is no abnormal signal in the thoracic spinal cord at this time. No compressive herniation, protrusion, lateral foraminal stenosis. Minimal degenerative disc disease in the thoracic spine. After contrast there is no abnormal enhancement or enhancing mass.

IMPRESSION:

Minimal degenerative disc disease. There is no evidence of demyelination. Complete resolution of abnormal lesion in the spinal cord at T2 level.

Before & After Comparison of MRIs of the Cervical Spine

In 2007, the MRI of the cervical spine showed loss of signal on all levels. The cervical area of her spine was unable to send and receive information to the rest of her body. A disk protrusion at C4-C5 eccentric to the left of her spine and prominent osteophytes, also called bone spurs, eccentric to the left at C5-C6 were also discovered. These are signs of disk degeneration disease and are frequently called 'bulging disks'.

The 2009 report below, showed one significant improvement: There is now normal signal in the cervical spine, which formally reported no signal. However, the protrusions remained about the same. This report directed us to put our healing emphasis on the cervical spine to affect improvement there as well.

REPORT STATUS: Final

PATIENT: , SHANA

SERVICE PROVIDED ON: 04/14/2009@1414

- -

NON-AFFILIATE INFO:

　　　　　PROCEDURE
　　　　　MR SPINE CERV W&W/O CONTRAST
- -

MR of the cervical spine without and with contrast 4/14/2009.

Clinical history: Multiple sclerosis. Numbness. Back pain. History of multiple sclerosis.

Comparison: 6/6/2007.

Multilevel degenerative disc disease. The craniocervical junction, C1-C2, C2-C3, C3-C4 levels are unremarkable.

At C4-C5 level, there is a broad-based left paracentral, mixed, spondylotic and soft disc, predominantly soft disc protrusion. This is mildly impinging the leftward cord. This is similar to the previous examination.

At C5-C6 level, there is of broad-based, spondylotic bony protrusion. This is also mildly compressing the central and leftward cord. There is also left-sided neural foraminal narrowing. This is similar to the previous examination.

At C6-C7 level, no compressive herniation. Minimal facet arthropathy.

The cervical spinal cord demonstrates normal signal. There is no abnormal enhancement after contrast. No prevertebral, paraspinal soft tissue swelling.

Impression:

1. No evidence of demyelinating disease in the cervical spine.

2. Broadbased central and left paracentral spondylotic and soft disc protrusion at C4-C5 compressing the leftward cord.

3. Broad-based left paracentral and central spondylotic bony protrusion compressing the central and left side of cord. There is also less side neural foraminal narrowing.

4. No significant change since 6/6/2007.

Appendix: Alice's Healing Timeline

My healing journey actually consisted of healing four different health issues during the same period of time. I wanted to give you a visual of the elapsed time between diagnosis, healing, and medical proof of wellness for each issue. For all but heavy metals, the healing transformation occurred rapidly, in only four to eight weeks. What often took longer was obtaining the medical proof. This chart spans from May of 2007, until May of 2008, with notes on my ongoing wellness.

MAY 2007	JUNE	JULY	AUGUST	OCTOBER	NOVEMBER	FEBUARY 2008	MAY	ONGOING
Diagnosis: Vagina Dysplasia	Healing Trans-formation	Medical Proof Improved					Medial Proof Healed	Continued Medical Confirmation July '09
		Diagnosis: Breast Cancer	Healing Trans-formation		Medical Proof No Cancer	Medical Confirmation No Cancer	Medical Confirmation No Cancer & Lump Gone	Continued Medical Confirmation Sept '08 & Mar '09
			Symptom Severe Stomach Disorder	Diagnosis: Parasites	Healing Trans-formation	Medical Proof Healed		
						Diagnosis: Heavy Metals		Healing Trans-formation Nov '08

A Message from the Author
Step onto Your Healing Path

You have read through my book, but what are you going to do now? Some may put it on a shelf. Some may actively tell others about what they learned. Some may do both, while incorporating the information into their daily routine.

I recommend the last course of action. This book was arranged so it would be useful as a reference book to keep on hand. Keep it in the kitchen, on your bedside table, or in your office. I hope that you refer to it often. It can help you! Please share it with as many other people as you can. You want all of your friends and family to be healthy, free of disease, and free of emotional issues, right? What a great gift to give for someone you love. Most importantly, however, is to step onto your healing path. Even if you feel perfectly healthy – mind, body, spirit, and emotions – the benefit is to prevent health issues and maintain health. This is especially true as you age.

Include the lifestyle practices described in this book as part of your life. If you have just healed a health issue, please do not go back to your old way of being. Make your healing lifestyle your permanent lifestyle. Let's stay healthy by staying on the healing path and making it your ongoing path.

If you want to improve your health or prevent disease, make the changes necessary to eliminate a worry and fear based life. Hold onto positive thoughts and emotions everyday. Get plenty of sleep and rest. Engage in an exercise routine that includes breath work. Establish a practice of meditation and eat healing organic foods with an emphasis on vegetables.

All healing is spiritual first. In fact, all of life is spiritual first. You are spirit living in your body. Your spirit, your soul, is who you are. Get to know that part of you. Learn to live in the present moment, letting your soul show you the way. Surrender your fears and set intentions for what you desire. Trust that God will take care of the rest. Then enjoy each day with joy. This is the best prescription for leading a long, healthy life, and it is so freeing and joyful. Please give it a try.

If this feels overwhelming, don't try to change and do everything all at once. Start incorporating healthy changes gradually. Perhaps you will be inspired to start by changing how you eat. Perhaps you will start incorporating regular meditation into your life, but please start.

I also want to discuss the financial aspect of my journey. Much of what is in this book is not covered by insurance, so it requires a change of perspective. You can co-pay for medicines and treatments your entire life, minimizing a pain or symptom, but often it lingers and gets worse. That small amount of money for your co-pay adds up, as do the negative side effects from many treatments. Additionally, it seems that most insurance policies are covering less and less each year.

I have estimated what it would have cost me to use traditional medical treatments, using my co-pay on my health insurance. It was a lot cheaper to heal naturally, even though I paid for most of it out of pocket. My expenses for healing dysplasia of the vagina, breast cancer, metal toxicity, and parasites, including my food, supplements, and much more, was less than 25% of what the estimated co-pay would have been for traditional medical costs for addressing breast cancer only. This approach not only healed my health issues without harmful side effects, it also allowed me to grow spiritually, mentally, and emotionally. The more costly traditional approach would have eliminated a breast and lymph nodes, which are now healthy and intact.

I learned that when you honor yourself by putting yourself and your health first, God and your angels will help with everything so it works out – including finances.

I hope that I have given you much to think about and consider. Remember that any investment you make in your health - mind, body, spirit, and emotion - will pay off in the long run. It's always a good investment to make.

I want to remind you of the intention I set the day I learned of my diagnosis: *"I will be guided and supported to heal myself successfully, so I can offer hope for others, and share what I learn."* This book is a manifestation of this intention. May it offer you hope and empowerment, as well as knowledge.

I intend for you much health, joy, peace, and happiness.

Love & Light –

Alice

Alice is available for sessions in person, and over the phone. Contact her at www.healingpath.info to learn more on how she can help you and those you love.

Appreciation

Special acknowledgement for those who were an integral and ongoing part of my healing journey:

Herbologist and Healer, Christopher Gilbert - Portland, OR

Acupuncture Physician, Rebecca Freeman – Shalimar, FL

Doctor of Naturopathy at Progressive Medical Center, Dr G. Agolli – Atlanta, GA

Feng Shui & Site Dowsing Consultant, Sharon Rothman – Bergenfield, NJ

Psychic Readers, Terry 'Graybear' Graybeal, Sarah Christopher, & Will Rosasco – Pensacola, FL

I also want to thank those who provided support and knowledge when needed:

Reiki, Sandy Trimble – Shalimar, FL, Shannon Faulk – DeFuniak Springs, FL, & Lisa Worsham, Navarre, FL

Pilates, Laurie Beck – Santa Rosa Beach, FL

Thermograms, Carol Cunningham - Tallahassee, FL

Organic Foods & Supplements, For the Health of It – Santa Rosa Beach, FL

Body Testing (Computer & Kinesiology), Dr. E. Johnson – Niceville, FL

Vibrational Protocols, Carolyn Libby – Lebanon, OR

Macrobiotic Counselor, Michael Rossoff – Ashville, NC

Medical Intuitives, Alexa Moffattt - Houston TX & Mary 'Kacey' Taylor - Fort Walton, FL

Yoga and Healing Oasis, Julie Wilcox - Santa Rosa Beach, FL

Colon Hydrotherapy, Michael Forman – Santa Rosa Beach, FL

Yoga and Breath Work, Carolyn Reynolds – Niceville, FL

Thanks to my friends Shana Spooner, Sarah Christopher, Lee Wilcox, my sister Ellen Zapalla, and my assistant Nikki Hedrick for content review, editing support and proof reading.

Additional thanks to Nikki Hedrick for page and cover formatting and design.

Also Available From Alice

CDs

"Your guided meditation helps me get out of my mind chatter. I feel I am in a special spot. My daily worries and heaviness always vanish, and I end feeling more energized and lighthearted." **CD, Dothan, AL**

Toning and Healing
Two separate guided mediations utilizing Alice's signature toning technique. The first is *"The Beach,"* a balancing journey that helps you release the negative thoughts and emotions you are holding on to, renewing you with the healing energy of the beach. The second meditation is *"The Reflective Pool,"* which helps you get in touch with your innermost heart and soul to discover inspiration that is unique for you.

Heart and Soul
This popular CD includes an inspirational talk, focusing on the importance of following your heart and listening to your soul. This is followed by a guided mediation that facilitates you to receive wisdom from you heart and soul. It will inspire you to start a practice of listening to your heart for guidance and decision-making!

Put Yourself First
Learn why it is not selfish, but smart to make yourself a priority. This inspirational talk includes practical tips for achieving this, even in your busy life. A guided meditation follows, to help you receive information on how to enhance your ability to honor and be true to yourself

Healthy Energy
Want to maintain your energy? Want to create a routine to help you feel balanced? Alice's "Healthy Energy" CD is a great maintenance program for you! The first track, "Daily Renewal" aims at helping you remain grounded, centered, and balanced. The second track, "Weekly Chakra Tuning" focuses deeply on your chakras and keeping them in optimal condition.

All meditations on Alice's CDs incorporate her signature toning to help you to stay out of your active thoughts and enjoy the core of you. Toning provides sound healing to your chakras and body. Alice also incorporates guided imagery and a mild regression to your heart to support your meditations.

Coming Soon: 'Wellness Wisdom for Your Beloved Pets'

Pet's can heal naturally too. Keta, Alice's beloved Yorkshire terrier was diagnosed with degenerative disk disease. Surgery or permanent crating with strong medications were the suggested solutions to this serious issue. The inspiring story of how Alice and Keta used the Wellness Wisdom principles to heal this issue is featured, along with other animal healing success stories.

This book will provide you with the detail needed to start bolstering your pet's health naturally and healing their health issues. Learn about healing foods and supplements for your pet, what foods are harmful for your pet, what holistic practices work for animals, and more.

We all love our pets. Their health and well-being is totally dependant on us. Finally, there is a source to assist us in giving them what they need to stay healthy and live longer - naturally!